Public Health Pests

Public Health Pests

A guide to identification, biology and control

N.R.H. Burgess
Defense Adviser in Entomology, Ministry of Defence, UK
and Senior Lecturer in Entomology

CHAPMAN AND HALL

LONDON • NEW YORK • TOKYO • MELBOURNE • MADRAS

UK	Chapman and Hall, 2–6 Boundary Row, London SE1 8HN
USA	Van Nostrand Reinhold, 115 5th Avenue, New York NY10003
JAPAN	Chapman and Hall Japan, Thomson Publishing Japan, Hirakawacho Nemoto Building, 7F, 1-7-11 Hirakawa-cho, Chiyoda-ku, Tokyo 102
AUSTRALIA	Chapman and Hall Australia, Thomas Nelson Australia, 480 La Trobe Street, PO Box 4725, Melbourne 3000
INDIA	Chapman and Hall India, R. Seshadri, 32 Second Main Road, CIT East, Madras 600 035

First edition 1990

© 1990 Chapman and Hall
Copyright for illustrations remains the property of Maurizia Merati

Typeset in 11/12½pt Palatino by EJS Chemical Composition,
Midsomer Norton, Bath, Avon
Printed in Great Britain by
St Edmundsbury Press, Bury St Edmunds, Suffolk

ISBN 0 412 32330 3

British Library Cataloguing in Publication Data

Burgess, N.R.H.
    Public health pests.
    1. Buildings. Pests. Control
    I. Title
    628.96

    ISBN 0 412 32330 3

Library of Congress Cataloguing-in-Publication Data

Available

To my wife Sue,
who has lived with me and my insects for over 30 years

Contents

Preface

The control of insects and other pests has long been an important aspect of public health in temperate and tropical parts of the world. Infestations, whether extensive or restricted, are cosmetically unacceptable and may become a medical hazard, particularly in the tropics and subtropics where a pest may also act as the carriers of disease. Flies, cockroaches, rats and mice can cause embarassment and financial loss to hotels, catering establishments and food manufacturers, even when they occur in small numbers.

Pesticides for use against these creatures are being continuously developed and, if used incorrectly, may present a hazard both to the user and to the general public. If not used efficiently, they will be ineffective and financially wasteful, and may result in the pest becoming resistant to them. Recent legislation, in particular the Food and Environment Protection Act (1985) and the resulting Control of Pesticides Regulations (1986), as well as the Health and Safety at Work etc Act (1974), with its regulations governing the Control of Substances Hazardous to Health (1988), makes it mandatory for those involved in the supply, storage, sale and/or use of pesticides to be properly trained and competent.

This manual is intended as a basic guide for those involved in all aspects of pest and vector control. It provides essential facts and useful information for those aiming to achieve the necessary standards of competence, and gives a firm foundation for further study.

We are most grateful to Killgerm Chemicals Ltd for their generous sponsorship of the colour plates.

1
Pest infestation

A pest may be defined as a creature which is undesirable in a particular situation, for reasons of health and hygiene, comfort and acceptability. The number of individual pests which renders them undesirable will depend on a particular situation. Therefore, 20 or 30 cockroaches in a hotel boiler room may be acceptable, whereas a single insect in a hospital operating theatre clearly is not. A critical customer might object to one fly in a restaurant; we would all object to one fly in our bowl of soup.

Pest species will be found in most parts of the world. Their relevance to public health will depend on the type and degree of their association with the human environment. Consideration must be given to the importance of a pest infestation relative to factors such as conditions of living, housing standards and the incidence of disease. For example, cockroach infestations in low cost housing in developing countries are often impossible to control; where sanitary conditions are poor, their significance as mechanical carriers of enteric disease may be critical. Standards of living, and hence expectations, are higher in developed countries.

The task of the pest control operator is to ensure that any infestation remains below the level of acceptability for whatever reason. In order to achieve this, an effective system of detection must be organized so that operators become aware of very low levels of pest infestation. They will thus be able to ensure that control measures are carried out before the infestation reaches unacceptable levels for the general public.

2

Pests

Animals in a number of groups may be regarded as pests for a variety of reasons. The most important groups are the insects and rodents, some of which (for example, flies, cockroaches and ants, rats and mice) create problems by occurring in large numbers in domestic situations, spoiling food and other material by their feeding habits, causing a nuisance and perhaps being involved in the transmission of infectious organisms. Other insects, such as moths and beetles, will feed on domestic fabrics and the structure of buildings, rendering them unusable or unsound. Rodents will behave in a similar manner, destroying food and structural materials and causing unhygienic conditions by their habits. Other vertebrates, birds and cats in particular, will be a nuisance when they occur in unacceptable situations or numbers.

Methods for controlling these pests are equally varied, but often the basic requirement of any control programme is to remove the factors necessary for the survival of the pest, namely shelter, warmth, food and water. This alone may be a sufficient control measure. However, when controlling rodents, improvements in hygiene should be initiated after control measures have been undertaken, since any interference with the environment prior to reduction in number disrupts the behaviour pattern of the pest.

Basic hygiene is vitally important in the control and avoidance of any infestation. The situation may be similarly alleviated by purely physical measures, such as the in-filling of harbourages, provision of correct food storage facilities, removal of water by repairing leaking pipes or installing better drainage and efficient pest proofing of doors and windows.

PEST CONTROL PROGRAMME

The control programme, for whatever pest, should always consist of five stages:

1. Survey
2. Planning
3. Control measures
4. Monitoring
5. Maintenance

Survey

It is impossible to control any pest efficiently until it has been correctly identified. It may not be essential to find the pest itself because it can often be identified from the damage it has caused, its faeces or other signs. However, a relevant and effective method of control can often only be carried out when an exact identification of the pest has been made, necessitating catching and identifying a specimen. Thus, the survey stage will include a detailed search of the infested area looking for relevant signs, the use of monitoring devices, such as cockroach sticky traps or rodent tracking powder, and the collection and identification of the pest at one or more stages of its life cycle. In order to do this competently, a knowledge of the characteristic features of the pest, its life cycle and habits is essential.

Planning

Once the problem has been identified, the measures required to control it can be determined. The survey will have shown if the infestation can be alleviated or even eradicated by improvements in hygiene, structural alterations or repairs. It may be necessary to use chemical or biological pesticides. At this stage the most effective active ingredients and methods of application can be assessed, the areas to be treated can be determined and the practical aspects considered. A pesticide which is most effective against the pest but least toxic to non-target organisms, including humans, should be selected. Also, minor factors, which nevertheless are essential to the eventual success of the operation, should be considered; for example, checking access to the site to be treated, warning residents or staff and ensuring that pesticides are not cleaned away before the pest can be affected.

Control measures

An efficient survey and comprehensive planning should ensure that the actual control measures are carried out quickly and effectively. The measures adopted will obviously depend on the pest to be controlled, and will be detailed under each of the relevant succeeding chapters. A record, probably in a pest control book, should give details of action taken, pesticides used etc.

Monitoring

It is important to determine the success or failure of control measures. This can be achieved visually, by observing the numbers of the pest at intervals after control, or by further use of monitoring devices such as sticky or other traps.

Maintenance

Most control measures should show a beneficial effect within a few days, but it will probably take longer to eradicate the problem hence follow up measures will often be necessary. Initial pesticide treatment may not, for example, affect insect eggs so that further treatment will be needed once they have hatched. By monitoring the situation, reinfestation, perhaps through reintroduction, can be detected and the necessary action taken before infestation exceeds the level of acceptability.

3

Pesticides

A pesticide is defined as a substance, chemical or otherwise, which kills a pest, acting on it in one or more ways. It may simply be a stomach poison (for example boric acid) which kills the pest when it takes it up; it may be absorbed by the pest through its skin or cuticle and kill it by disorganizing its nervous or vascular system (DDT and malathion); it may dehydrate the pest (silica) or affect its reproductive system (methoprene).

Most pesticides are synthetic chemicals, although some of the earlier ones were derived from natural substances, and more recent ones are synthesized components identical to those naturally produced by the animal itself.

PEST CONTROL LEGISLATION IN BRITAIN

Until 1985, the vast majority of pesticides in Britain were registered voluntarily by the manufacturer under the Pesticides Safety Precautions Scheme (PSPS), supported by the Ministry of Agriculture, Food and Fisheries (MAFF). An approval with a PSPS number was only granted if the pesticide attained certain standards, particularly in reference to its safety to the user and non-target organisms, and the comprehensiveness of the container label.

In 1985, the Food and Environment Protection Act (FEPA) came into force, followed in 1986 by its Control of Pesticides Regulations (COPR). Under FEPA and COPR all pesticides were required by law to be approved under the Act, and the approval also required evidence of efficacy. Pesticides were divided into two groups: those used for agricultural purposes (including horticulture, industrial herbicides, forestry and use in or near water), and those used for other purposes (including public health, wood preservation, animal husbandry, fumigation and masonry biocides).

Those storing, supplying or using a pesticide must by law only use one that is approved under FEPA and must be competent to carry out those duties. This requirement necessitates proper training, and an assessment of the effectiveness of that training. At this moment, however, only those persons involved with pesticides classified as agricultural are required to be certificated. It is perhaps impractical to attempt to ensure competence without the rational follow up of assessment by some form of examination, which the trainee must pass in order to prove competence. The award of a certificate is tangible proof of this achievement.

By law, all pesticide containers must carry a comprehensive label which, in addition to other details, must include information regarding the active ingredient, target pests, instructions for mixing, application and disposal, and safety precautions. Thus the label is the 'bible' for that pesticide, and it is essential that anyone involved with the pesticide should read the label carefully.

Further legislation covering the storage, use and disposal of pesticides, and requirement for competence of operators, is included in the *Control of Substances Hazardous to Health (COSHH) Regulations (1988)* or the *Health and Safety at Work Act (1974)*.

PEST CONTROL LEGISLATION IN OTHER COUNTRIES

Pest control products in the USA are categorized as 'restricted' or 'general'. Training conferring 'certified application status' is only mandatory for the use of restricted products as defined by the Environmental Protection Agency (EPA), the federal organization whose approval is required for all pest control products. Legislation for which EPA has been responsible since its formation in 1970 was originally enshrined in the Federal Insecticide, Fungicide and Rodenticide Act (FIFRA), 1947. This was amended on several occasions and completely revised in the Federal Environmental Pesticide Control Act (FEPCA), 1972, which itself has had a number of amendments. Legislation within each State may restrict the use of certain pesticides even if they are approved by EPA. Similar legislation is in force in many developed countries, for example, in the Netherlands: Pesticides Order (1980), Order on the Composition, Classification, Packaging and Labelling of Pesticides (1980); and in the Federal Republic of Germany (West Germany): paragraph 10C of the Federal Communicable Diseases

Act, 1979. Many other countries, for example Hong Kong, are attempting to bring their standards into line with these.

PESTICIDE APPLICATION

Pesticides may be applied in a variety of ways according to their formulation and mode of action. The most important requirement is that the pesticide should be applied in such a way and to such an environment that the pest will easily and effectively come into contact with it, and that the pesticide should remain in that environment long enough to be effective, but that the environment itself and non-target organisms within it should not be damaged. Thus the habits of the pest concerned, the activity and residual effect of the pesticide, and the supervision of the site after treatment are important factors to be considered.

Formulations and methods of application will be discussed in the relevant sections under insecticides, rodenticides and other specific methods of control.

SAFETY PRECAUTIONS

Pesticides are essentially toxic substances, but their commercial development and regulatory approval will ensure that this toxicity is directed against the pest itself and is minimal to the user and non-target organisms, provided that the pesticide is used according to the manufacturer's instructions. The hazard due to a pesticide is a product of its toxicity and depends on the duration of exposure. These have been approved by the regulatory body and are required by law to appear on the container label. It is thus essential for any user to read the label. These safety precautions will include details of the type of protective clothing required for handling, mixing and applying the material, any specific precautions required and the action to be taken in case of emergency.

The Pesticide Register is produced regularly and provides up to date details of pesticides which have been approved by the Advisory Committee on Pesticides (MAFF and HSE).

Certain basic rules refer to the use of all pesticides:

1. Read the label

2. Only use the pesticide for the purpose(s) and in the way described on the label

3. Use the protective clothing as suggested

4. Do not eat, drink or smoke in any area where pesticides are being stored, transported, mixed or applied

5. Dispose of unwanted pesticide and containers correctly (as detailed in MAFF booklet No 2198 (1987) and summarized in Appendix A)

6. Wash hands and clean protective clothing after touching pesticides

7. Store pesticides correctly (as detailed in HSE Guidance Note CS19 (1988) and summarized in Appendix B)

8. Ensure medical assistance is available in case of emergency

HSE Guidance Notes MS17 (biological monitoring of workers exposed to organophosphorus pesticides) and EH 40/88 (occupational exposure limits) may be referred to.

4

Insect control

Insects can be controlled in a variety of ways: by physical methods, application of chemical insecticides and use of biological insecticides. It should always be remembered that it may not be necessary to use insecticides at all in order to control an infestation. This can often be achieved by purely physical methods, such as the removal of harbourages and breeding sites or improvements in hygiene. In any case, physical methods should always be incorporated in any pest control exercise.

INSECTICIDES

Literally defined, an insecticide is any material which kills insects. The ideal insecticide is one which kills insects quickly and effectively at moderately low concentration, without affecting the environment or non-target organisms. It should not be toxic to humans, should be easy to apply and inexpensive. There may frequently be situations where insects can be controlled by purely physical means, without the use of insecticides, and these should always be given prime consideration.

Insecticides are conveniently divided into chemical compounds (see below) and biological compounds (see page 17).

Chemical insecticides

Chemical insecticides act in two ways:

1. As *stomach poisons*: These are taken up by the insect in the form of a bait, or may be applied to surfaces over which the insect will walk, taking up the material on its legs and body. This will then be taken into the alimentary canal when the insect cleans itself.

2. As *contact poisons*: These may be applied to the atmosphere through which the insect is flying, or to surfaces over which it will walk. The chemical penetrates the cuticle or enters the spiracles and, depending on the active ingredient, will act on the nervous system by disrupting nerve impulses, causing uncoordinated behaviour followed by paralysis and death of the insect. Contact insecticides can be divided into those which have an immediate 'knockdown-and-kill' effect but no persistent action and those which have a 'residual' effect which may last for several weeks.

A further type of contact insecticide will affect the wax layer of the cuticle, causing the insect to become dehydrated.

Chemical insecticides are grouped as follows:

Pyrethrins
The earliest insecticides were naturally occurring chemical components of plants. Of those, the best known is pyrethrum, derived from Chrysanthemum flowers. Pyrethrum consists of pyrethrins and cinerins and is still in use as a 'knockdown' insecticide. Its action requires enhancement by the addition of a synergist, piperonyl butoxide, to make it act more rapidly. It is effective against a wide range of insects (not necessarily an advantage, as more selective insecticides are often preferable) but is virtually harmless to humans and other mammals. Its residual activity is minimal, and the active ingredients break down in sunlight. Perhaps most significantly, this insecticide is now very expensive to produce, relying as it does on the natural cultivation of certain species of flowers in confined parts of the world.

Organochlorine compounds (chlorinated hydrocarbons)
The insecticidal properties of organochlorine (OC) compounds were first noted before World War II, and were used extensively in the 1940s. A few are still used today, although their application is severely restricted in many parts of the world. While being effective against many insects, organochlorine insecticides also have a high mammalian toxicity and a considerable residual action, often remaining effective for months or even years. This has resulted in the chemical being taken up in the food chain of many mammals, including humans. Adverse public and medical reaction to this has caused many of the OC compounds to be withdrawn except, for example, in the treatment of timber.

This group of chemicals is often the cheapest to produce commercially and the most immediately effective, and some are still in everyday use in many developing countries. There the insecticidal effects and cost have to be balanced against the possible environmental damage and mammalian toxicity, but more importantly against the often devastating results, medical or agricultural, of not controlling the pest.

Organochlorine compounds include DDT (dichlorodiphenyl-trichlorethane), BHC (the gamma isomer of benzene hexachloride, also known as HCH and commercially as lindane), dieldrin and chlordane. Many groups of insects have shown resistance (see page 22) to a number of OC insecticides.

Organophosphorus compounds

Organophosphorus (OP) compounds were developed in the 1940s and 1950s, with substances such as parathion and aldrin used particularly against agricultural pests. They were further developed for use in public health (for example, malathion, fenitrothion, diazinon). These compounds are effective against a wide range of insects as well as pest species, although their mammalian toxicity is generally not as high as the OC compounds, and often very much lower (for example, malathion and temephos).

OPs are usually more expensive to produce, but their residual life is shorter because they break down (metabolize) into harmless compounds before they can enter the food chain (i.e. they are biodegradable). Their relative toxicity to humans necessitates strict handling precautions, since excessive contact may cause cholinesterase inhibition (see Chapter 4) which, in fact, is how OPs kill insects. Many insects show resistance to OPs.

Carbamate compounds

Developed from the late 1950s, these compounds (for example bendiocarb, carbaryl, propoxur) are essentially esters of carbamic acid and act in a similar way to the OPs. However, the cholinesterase inhibition is reversible, thus rendering them less toxic to mammals but also enabling insects to recover from a sublethal dose. Nevertheless, some (for example bendiocarb) are very toxic to fish and cats, and require particular care in their use.

Pyrethroids
These synthetic compounds, developed mainly in the 1960s and 1970s (although allethrum was available as early as 1949), are chemically similar to natural pyrethrins. Most have a low mammalian toxicity but are effective against a range of insects, having a combination of knockdown and residual effects depending on the compound. Because of safety in use and ecological acceptability, this group has been extensively developed in recent years, but products are relatively expensive. Active ingredients include permethrin, allethrin, resmethrin and other compounds.

Composition of insecticides

The part of the insecticide which kills the insect is known as the 'active ingredient'. This will be mixed with a substance to enable it to be packaged and later diluted (the carrier). The active ingredient will have a chemical name (for example, bendiocarb) and often a very long compound name (for example 2.2-dimethyl-1, 3-benzodromol-t-yl methylcarbonate).

When packaged, the active ingredient will be sold under a trade name which will indicate the concentration and formulation, for instance *Ficam W*, which is an 80% concentration of bendiocarb mixed with a carrier of diatomaceous earths formulated for use as a wettable (water dispersible) powder. The container label will give prominence to the commercial name, but by law it must always include the other details. Some active ingredients, for example permethrin, will be used by a number of manufacturers in several commercial products. It is thus important to ensure that the user is aware of the active ingredient in the insecticide in question.

The technical grade insecticide is the purest commercial form of the active ingredient. This may be diluted in a solid or liquid carrier, dissolved in a solvent such as kerosene to form a solution and be combined with an emulsifier to form an emulsion. A mixture in certain proportions of solvent and emulsifier will form a flowable concentrate. Spreading or wetting agents may also be added, to encourage the diluted insecticide to cover the surface which is to be treated. A synergist may be added to some formulations, to enhance the insecticidal effect of the active ingredient.

The concentration or amount of insecticide or other pesticide (lethal concentration) needed to kill half of a known population of

Table 4.1 Oral and dermal toxicity ratings for selected pesticides (in mg of pesticide per kg body weight)

Chemical compound	Oral LD50	Dermal LD50
Abate	1000	1400
Bendiocarb	179	1000
BHC	200	—
Carbaryl	500	4000
Diazinon	76	455
DDT	118	2510
Dichlorvos	56	75
Dieldrin	46	60
Fenitrothion	250	700
Fenthion	245	330
Lindane	91	900
Malathion	1000	4444
Permethrin	500–3000	2500–4000

insects or other animals (usually in the laboratory) is known as the LC50. The lethal dose is similarly known as the LD50, and is the amount of insecticide or other pesticide expressed in mg per kg of body weight of the target animal, needed to kill 50% of a known population of that animal. It is obtained by administering it orally or dermally to laboratory animals. The terms 'acute' or 'chronic' indicate whether insecticide was administered in one single dose or over a period of time. LD50s of some recent and currently used insecticides are shown in Table 4.1.

Insecticide formulations

An insecticide can only be effective if the insect comes in contact with it in the intended way. Active ingredients are formulated with this in mind.

Space-spray concentrates
In order to develop a fog or aerosol for an area in which insects are flying, the active ingredient is typically mixed with kerosene and the mixture vaporized by a strong current of hot or cold air (see also page 18), or by passing it over a hot surface. Depending on the mechanism, the resulting particles will vary in size but will

average 50 microns (one micron is one-hundredth of a millimetre) or less in diameter. Smaller particles of 1–15 microns may be produced by specialized equipment and dispersed at ultra-low volume (ULV). This technique has the advantage of reducing the amount of carrier used and hence the bulk of diluted insecticide to be carried.

Misting

A similar formulation applied with different equipment (see page 19) produces larger particles (50–100 microns), forming a heavier mist which settles evenly on to surfaces over which insects will walk and hence come in contact with it.

Wettable powders

The active ingredient is often mixed with a carrier (of diatomaceous earths) and a wetting agent to form a solid powder, known as a wettable powder (WP) or water-dispersible powder (WDP). When mixed in water, the powder forms a suspension of very small insecticidal particles which are sprayed through a compression sprayer on surfaces where insects will walk (Plate 1). The container must be agitated before spraying, to avoid settling of the powder.

WPs are particularly useful on porous surfaces where the water content is absorbed, leaving the particles of active ingredient on the surface to come into contact with the insect. The much smaller particles of active ingredient in an emulsion concentrate would be absorbed with the carrier, leaving nothing on the surface.

Emulsion concentrates

The active ingredient dissolved in a solvent and mixed with an emulsifier forms an emulsion concentrate (EC), usually a thick oily liquid. This can be diluted by adding to water and mixing vigorously and dispersed over water surfaces (for mosquito larval control) or solid surfaces (on which insects will crawl or stand). The normal method of dispersal is through a compression sprayer, and the diluent must be agitated regularly to prevent separation of the concentrate from the water.

ECs are particularly useful for spraying non-porous surfaces to which they stick more readily than wettable powders, but they will often mark these surfaces because of the nature of the carrier (Plate 2).

Dusts

The active ingredient may be mixed with an inert dust or talc to form a dust or powder which can then be applied to surfaces, using a puffer or dust gun. The insect will take up the insecticide and be poisoned when it preens itself, or may enter through the cuticle or spiracles. Some formulations will damage the cuticle itself.

Dusts are of particular use for application in inaccessible areas such as ducting, and also for places in which liquid insecticides cannot be used, such as switch boxes, refrigerator motors and other electrical equipment where, for example, cockroaches may be harbouring. Powders are sometimes used for personal application (anti-louse powders) or on domestic animals.

Smoke generators

The active ingredient may be mixed in a pellet or container with smoke-producing chemicals. When ignited, the cloud of carbon particles will carry the insecticide and settle on horizontal surfaces. Smoke generators have a limited use in confined spaces such as lofts and silos.

Baits

An active ingredient can be incorporated into a material which provides attractive food for the insect. Domestic infestations usually occur because food is readily available to the pest; this factor must be removed before the bait can become effective.

Baits are particularly useful where widespread application of insecticide is undesirable, since they can be confined in containers which are only accessible to the particular pest.

Biological insecticides

The main disadvantage of chemical insecticides is their potential toxicity to humans and non-target organisms (i.e. their lack of specificity).

Insect pheromones

Considerable progress is currently being made in the synthesis of analogues of some of the complex chemicals (pheromones) produced by the insect itself, which govern its behaviour. These may take the form of sex attractants and aggregation pheromones which, for example, draw insects to a poison bait or a physical trap.

They may also be applied as insect growth regulator pheromones (IGRs) which will in some way affect the development of the insect.

IGRs are of several types; one will disrupt the development of larval stages to the pupa and adult (methoprene in mosquito and flea control). Methoprene may be taken in a bait by a worker Pharaoh ant to the nest, affecting the reproductive capacity of the queens when fed to them. Another type of growth regulator, hydroprene, will affect the development of cockroaches. By their very nature and the way in which they are applied, these materials will only affect the target species.

Bacteria
Certain bacteria, for example *Bacillus thuringiensis* and *B sphaericus*, will affect the alimentary canal of specific groups of immature insects, thus killing them. By careful application to the breeding sites of these insects, for example, mosquitoes or biting black fly (*Simulium*), effective control can be achieved.

Future biological methods will perhaps provide the safest and most effective pest control. Considerable research and development is required. New, commercially available materials, while being ecologically highly acceptable, are relatively expensive and take several weeks to achieve control.

Application methods

However effective the insecticide, it will only kill insects if it is properly applied so that it will come in contact with the insect. The method of application will depend to a large extent on the insecticide formulation to be used, which will in turn have been determined by other factors such as the pest to be controlled, the situation in question and environmental considerations.

Aerosol dispenser
The active ingredient in a carrier, usually kerosene, is contained in a pressurized can with an inert gas as the propellant (Fig. 4.1). The insecticide is released as a fog of particles about 50 microns in diameter which will remain airborne for several minutes, killing by knockdown action any insects coming in contact with the fog. Aerosols releasing a larger size of particle (50–100 microns) may be used for spraying a mist of residual insecticide over surfaces. Aerosol insecticides are also used for 'flushing out' insects from

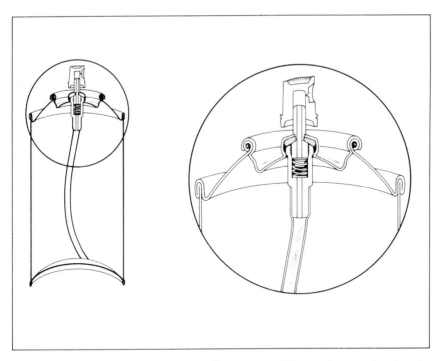

Fig. 4.1 Cross section of an aerosol container. The spring mechanism is shown in detail.

harbourages during a survey, as the insecticide often has an excitatory effect.

Fogging and misting
Fogs and mists, including ULV applications, can be created in a variety of ways. Particles of the required size range are formed, for example, by forcing the diluent under pressure through a small hole or over rotating discs or cups, by driving the diluent over electrically heated elements (Plate 3) or the hot exhaust ports of a petrol motor (Plate 4). A considerable range of fogging and misting equipment is commercially available, suitable for all sizes and types of operation. All good equipment is supplied with a comprehensive user's handbook which should be studied in detail.

Compression sprayer
Sprayers for dispensing emulsion concentrates or wettable powders are usually cylindrical, of 5–10 litres (1–2 gallons)

capacity, and made of stainless steel or moulded plastic. Using a hand-operated plunger pump incorporated in the cylinder, the diluted insecticide is compressed to the desired pressure (20–80 psi, depending on the model and application), which can be read from a pressure gauge in most models. For spraying solid surfaces a pressure of 20 psi is recommended, for soft (fabric) surfaces 40 psi, and for crack and crevice spraying 7–10 psi.

The insecticide is loaded by unscrewing the pump from the cylinder. The cylinder should be half-filled with water before adding the concentrated insecticide and topping up, otherwise the first part of the spray will be almost pure active ingredient, particularly with emulsion concentrates. A safety valve is usually fitted to avoid over-compression. The jet of insecticide is released through a flexible hose and rigid lance by depressing a trigger mechanism on the lance. The spray pattern and size of particle can be adjusted by using different jets.

The sprayer is carried on the back or over one shoulder, hence the alternative name of 'knapsack sprayer', although this name may refer to equipment in which the insecticide is actually pumped out of the container using the continuous action of a handle whilst spraying is in operation.

A compression sprayer is the basic tool of the pest control operator. It is efficient and easy to maintain, with few moving parts. The cylinder, hose and lance must be cleaned and all insecticide removed at the end of an operation to avoid corrosion and damage to the pump, washers and jet. Leaking hose junctions can be a potential hazard to the operation.

Dust gun

In the simple models, insecticidal dust is impelled from a reservoir container through a nozzle, by pumping on a handle or turning a rotor blade. Larger equipment may be driven by an electric or petrol motor. In this way dust can be driven into ducts and dead spaces which might otherwise be difficult to treat.

Traps

These take many forms:

Sticky traps: The simplest type is a cardboard 'tent' or box (Fig. 4.2) the floor of which is coated with a strong non-drying adhesive. Insects are attracted to the harbourage of the box, sometimes by the addition of an attractant pheromone or other bait, and become

Plate 1 Applying wettable powder insecticide from a compression sprayer, onto absorbent surfaces.

Plate 2 Applying emulsion concentrate insecticide from a compression sprayer, onto non-absorbent surfaces. Note the range of protective clothing used; gloves should also be worn.

Plate 3 Electric plate which heats a pad of insecticide. The vapour kills mosquitoes and other flying insects.

Plate 4 Fogging a kitchen. Safety precautions are particularly important in this confined environment. Protective clothing should be worn, pilot flames on equipment should be turned out and exit be accessible.

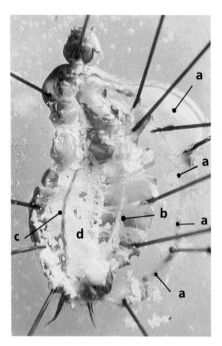

Plate 6 Adult *Periplaneta americana*, the American cockroach.

Plate 5 Dissected cockroach to show internal anatomy: (a) alimentary canal; (b) ventral nerve-cord; (c) dorsal tubular heart; (d) fat body.

Plate 7 *Periplaneta americana* moulting a nymphal skin. Several nymphal stages and adult can be seen.

Plate 8 Cockroaches (*Blatta orientalis*) feeding at night on dustbin refuse spilt on a kitchen floor. The bin should not have been left open or in the kitchen overnight.

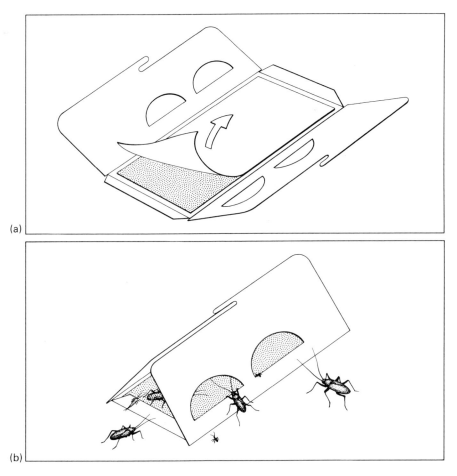

Fig. 4.2 A sticky trap of the 'tent' type. (a) the floor is coated with an adhesive; (b) insects are attracted to the harbourage of the box and become stuck to the floor.

stuck to the adhesive. Sticky traps are essentially for use in monitoring an infestation rather than controlling it, and are particularly useful in cockroach control programmes.

Pheromone traps: Insects, especially pests of stored products, are attracted into a container where they are physically trapped (Fig. 4.3).

Ultraviolet light traps: Used to kill flying insects, particularly houseflies and bluebottles. The fly is attracted to the light from an

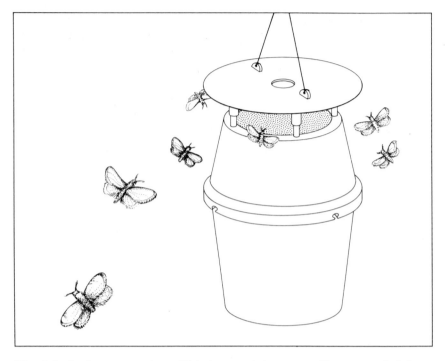

Fig. 4.3 A pheromone trap. This is a container, usually suspended from the ceiling, which attracts and traps insects.

ultraviolet tube and killed when it comes into contact with a high voltage electric grid placed in front of the tube. The dead insect is collected in a tray below the grid. Traps must be correctly sited away from competing daylight or fluorescent tube lighting; nevertheless they will collect only a proportion of flies present.

Insecticide resistance

A proportion of any insect population will have the genetic ability to tolerate (i.e. not be affected by) a specified amount of a particular insecticide. This is known as 'insecticide resistance' and will survive the control measures, reproducing a population with a greater proportion of resistant insects. Over several generations, the whole population may become resistant and can no longer be controlled by that particular insecticide. Resistance to one insecticide may confer resistance to another in the same chemical group or even in another group; this is known as 'cross-resistance'.

Failure to control an infestation should not immediately be attributed to insecticide resistance. It is much more likely that the fault lies in incorrect dilution of the insecticide or poor application techniques.

Occasionally, behavioural rather than genetic resistance may occur where the insect has developed the ability to avoid contact with the insecticide by altering its habits.

5

Insects

Many of the pests which require control belong to the largest of all animal groups, the Phylum Arthropoda. This phylum contains the Class Insecta (insects), the Class Arachnida (spiders, scorpions, ticks and mites), the Chilopoda (centipedes), the Diplopoda (millipedes) and the Crustacea (Fig. 5.1).

All arthropods have several characteristics in common, in particular a skeleton on the outside of the body (exoskeleton) which is segmented, with a pair of jointed appendages (legs, antennae etc) on most segments. Male and female are distinct. The Insecta form by far the largest of the arthropod classes, with over a million different species in a vast range of environments throughout most parts of the world.

EXTERNAL AND INTERNAL ANATOMY

The body of all insects is divided into three parts: the head, the thorax and the abdomen (Fig. 5.2). The head always bears one pair of antennae (sensory organs), the mouthparts and usually a pair of

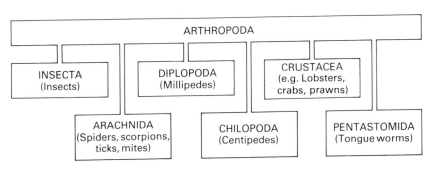

Fig. 5.1 Classification of the Phylum Arthropoda.

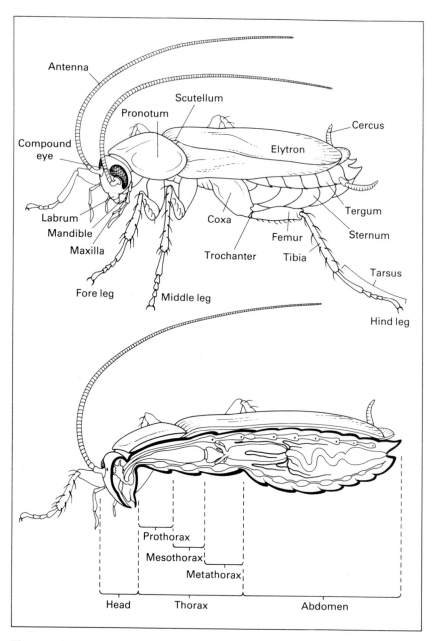

Fig. 5.2 The external anatomy of a cockroach (upper); in cross section, the head, thorax and abdomen are seen (lower).

eyes (simple or compound). The thorax bears three pairs of legs in the adult insect, and usually two pairs of wings (occasionally only one). This is the strongest and most rigid part of the body and contains the muscles of locomotion and flight. The abdomen is usually the bulkiest part of the body but rarely has appendages except for paired sensory organs at the posterior.

The internal anatomy consists of the alimentary canal running from the mouth to the anus through fore, mid and hind gut (Fig. 5.3). The mouthparts are paired organs which may be adapted for chewing, sucking or piercing tissue, depending on the diet of the species concerned. Salivary glands open into the mouth (buccal cavity). Most of the digestion of food is carried out in the mid-gut, although fluid may sometimes be regurgitated externally on to the food material to assist digestion. Water is often conserved in the hind gut and returned to the hollow body cavity which contains a clear fluid, the haemolymph. This fluid serves to transport nutrients around the body cavity, but is not involved in the movement of oxygen or carbon-dioxide as it does not contain haemoglobin (except in *Chironomus* species). Waste material is removed from the body cavity by means of the malpighian tubules (blind-ending tubes in the body space which open into the hind gut), from where it is evacuated in the form of faeces.

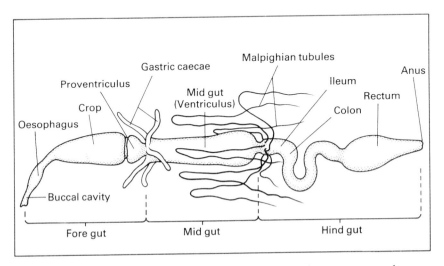

Fig. 5.3 The internal anatomy of a cockroach: the alimentary canal.

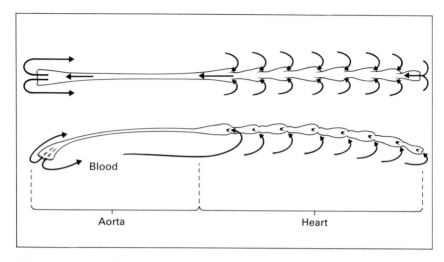

Fig. 5.4 Internal anatomy of a cockroach: the circulatory system. Top: horizontal section; bottom: side view. Arrows: haemolymph blood flow.

Body fluid is kept moving by a dorsal tubular heart (Fig. 5.4) which pumps it forward, although there is no vascular system as such.

The nervous system, consisting of paired ventral nerve cords fusing segmentally to form ganglia, is enlarged at the head to form the brain (Fig. 5.5).

Male and female sexes are separate (Fig. 5.6). Mating occurs by copulation, the male sperm often being stored by the female in a

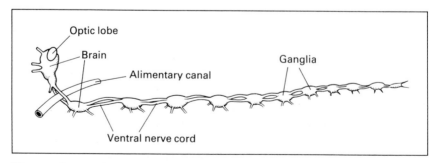

Fig. 5.5 Internal anatomy of a cockroach: the nervous system.

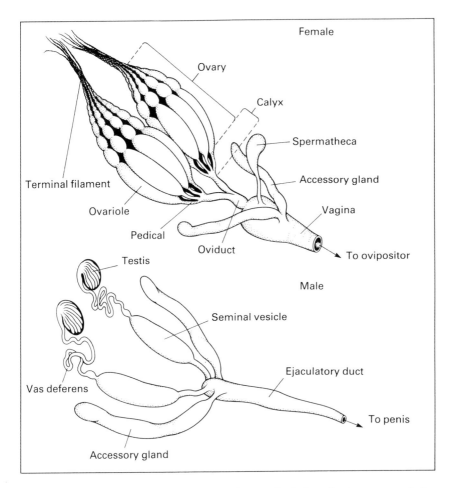

Fig. 5.6 The reproductive system of a typical female insect, and the genital system of a male insect.

sperm sac, the spermatheca, for subsequent fertilization of the ova. This means that the female insect may only need to mate once during her adult life, but can produce several batches of eggs.

Air will enter holes (spiracles) on either side of the body, which lead to a system of tubes (tracheae) spreading throughout the body (Fig. 5.7). The tracheae supply all parts with oxygen and assist in the removal of waste carbon dioxide.

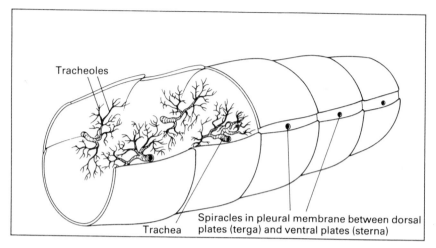

Tracheoles

Spiracles in pleural membrane between dorsal
plates (terga) and ventral plates (sterna)

Trachea

Fig. 5.7 The respiratory system of a typical insect.

INSECT CLASSIFICATION AND GENERALIZED LIFE CYCLES

The Class Insecta is divided into two subclasses (Fig. 5.8), the smaller of which contains insects which have never had wings at any stage of their evolution and go through very little change in appearance (metamorphosis) during their development. This is the subclass Apterygota (Greek: *a* = without; *pteron* = wing) which is in turn divided into four Orders, one of which, the Collembola, contains the silverfish, an insect of minor public health importance.

The other subclass, the Pterygota, contains insects which have one or two pairs of wings or have lost them in the course of their evolution, often due to a parasitic way of life, and have become secondarily wingless. The Pterygota are further divided into two groups depending on the type of life cycle or metamorphosis through which they pass.

In one group, the creature which hatches from the egg looks very like the adult except that it is much smaller, does not have wings and cannot reproduce. By passing through a series of moults, during which the hard exoskeleton is cast off, the insect expands a new elastic exoskeleton by taking in air and the new skin hardens and darkens in colour. The insect is able to grow in size and will pass through a number of these nymphal stages, punctuated by

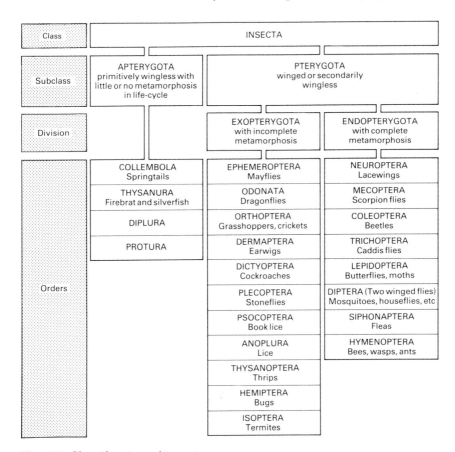

Fig. 5.8 Classification of insects.

moults, until it reaches maturity. Only after the final moult will wings appear. The change in appearance is not complete, hence this type of life cycle is described as showing an incomplete metamorphosis. Wings develop outside the exoskeleton, hence the group is sometimes called the Exopterygota (Greek: *exo* = outside; *pteron* = wing).

The other type of life cycle shows a complete metamorphosis. From the egg hatches a creature which in no way resembles the adult. This is the feeding and growing stage known as the larva; it will pass through a series of moults in order to increase its size. When the larva is fully grown it will form a hard skin around itself, the pupa, inside which it will disintegrate and reconstruct itself into the adult form. The pupa does not feed and is typically sessile.

It is the success of the larval stage in finding adequate food which will govern the size of the adult insect, since no growth can occur after pupation. A underfed larva will produce a small adult insect. The adult insect will emerge from the pupal case inside which the wings have been formed, hence the name for this group, the Endopterygota (Greek: *endo* = inside; *pteron* = wing).

Whilst it may seem that this second type of life cycle is very complex, it has the great advantage that at least two different environments can be utilized by the insect. The egg will hatch only when a larval food supply is available; when the food supply disappears, the larva will pupate and the adult will emerge to make use of a different environment. This advantage is borne out by the fact that 85% of all insect species pass through a complete metamorphosis in their life cycle.

A basic classification of the Class Insecta is given in Figure 5.8 which shows the more important Orders within each group. Reference should be made to this classification when studying specific insects in succeeding chapters.

Orders containing insects of public health importance include the following:

Exopterygota

Dictyoptera (cockroaches)

Anoplura (sucking lice)

Hemiptera (bedbugs)

Endopterygota

Diptera (including mosquitoes and other bloodsucking midges; horseflies, houseflies, bluebottles and other flies)

Siphonaptera (fleas)

Hymenoptera (bees, wasps, ants etc)

Coleoptera (beetles, including pests of stored products and wood-boring pests)

The recognition, life cycle, habits, public health significance and control of each of the groups will be discussed in succeeding chapters.

Specific names

All living organisms have two scientific names, the genus and the species, in addition to their common name. Examples are *Blattella* (genus: always written with an capital initial letter) *germanica* (species: written with a small initial letter), e.g. the German cockroach, or *Cimex lectularius*, the bedbug. These names refer only to that particular species and no other, whereas common names are often misleading, referring to one insect in one country and a different insect in another. The genus and species are always printed in italics or should be underlined, for instance when writing reports in longhand. A species can reproduce with members of the same species but not with those of another species.

6

Dictyoptera (cockroaches)

There are some 4000 species of cockroach throughout most parts of the world. They are a very ancient group, first appearing in fossils 250 million years old, and have changed little in appearance since then. The vast majority are tropical or subtropical and have little or no contact with humans. However, a few species, perhaps no more than a dozen, have become adapted to the human environment and, although tropical in origin, have colonized and flourished in artificial pseudotropical situations. These include the three most important species: *Blattella germanica* (the German Cockroach), *Blatta orientalis* (the Oriental Cockroach), and *Periplaneta americana* (the American Cockroach), and other less important species such as *Periplaneta australasiae* (the Australian Cockroach) and *Supella longipalpa* (the Brown-Banded Cockroach).

GENERAL DESCRIPTION

Adult pest species of cockroach may vary in size from 10–50 mm (up to 2 inches) in length. Plate 5 shows the internal anatomy of the cockroach. The body is flattened from top to bottom (dorso-ventrally) and clearly divided into head, thorax and abdomen. The front dorsal part of the thorax is usually well developed and the head is slung below this, often partially obscured from above (Fig. 6.1). Cockroaches typically have long filamentous antennae, one pair of eyes, and chewing mouthparts adapted for omnivorous feeding, slung ventrally.

The well developed thorax holds three pairs of strong legs, often covered in stout hairs or bristles, terminating in paired claws and sometimes a pad (pulvillus). Adult cockroaches in most species have two pairs of well developed wings with a webbed venation (Greek: *dictos* = web; hence Dictyoptera) folded scissor-like over

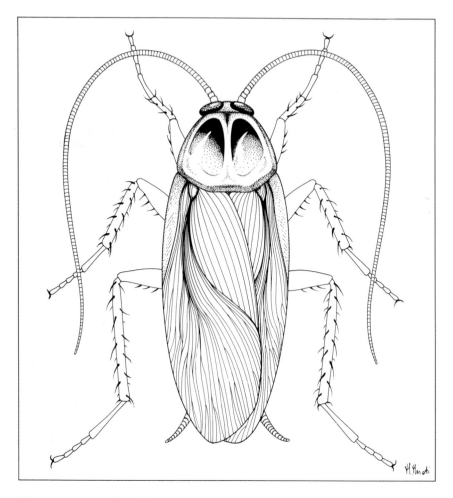

Fig. 6.1 An adult cockroach. Its external features are depicted here from above.

the thorax and abdomen. Winged cockroaches in the tropics may fly actively at night, but cooler temperatures in temperate regions will rarely activate the wing muscles sufficiently to allow flight. A few species, particularly *B orientalis*, have greatly reduced wings and thus never fly. The abdomen of the cockroach is obviously segmented and only has appendages in the form of cerci at the hind end.

LIFE CYCLE

This is one of incomplete metamorphosis. The Dictyoptera (cockroaches and mantids) differ from all other insects in that the female lays her eggs in a case (ootheca) containing 12–50 eggs, depending on the species (Table 6.1). These oothecae are very resistant to dessication and also to the ingress of insecticides (see page 48). From the egg will hatch the first-stage nymph, a wingless miniature of the adult. On hatching, the exoskeleton is pale in colour and soft, but within minutes it darkens and hardens, a process known as tanning undergone by all hatching or moulting insects. The cockroach may pass through a number of nymphal stages during its life cycle, 5–12 depending on the species, before the final moult to the adult.

Table 6.1 Distinguishing features for oothecae of the most common species of cockroaches

Species	Size (mm)	Number of segments	Raised areas below keel	Diagram
Blattella germanica	8 × 3	18	None	
Blatta orientalis	10 × 5	None	8–9, circular	
Periplaneta americana	8 × 5	None	8–9, elongate	
Periplaneta australasiae	10 × 5	None	12–13	
Supella supellectilium	4 × 25	8	None	

Habits

All cockroach stages, nymphal and adult, will feed on a wide range of substances, particularly refuse and human food. A source of moisture is most important, and cockroaches will not live for more than a few weeks without water, whereas they can survive for several months without food.

Being flattened dorsoventrally, cockroaches are able to utilize narrow cracks and crevices as harbourages. They will remain hidden in these during the day, only coming out in darkness to feed. This nocturnal habit means that, except in heavy infestations, they will not be apparent during the hours of daylight. Most species move quickly and climb with ease.

Some fifty species of cockroach in different parts of the world have acquired the habit of domestication to a greater or lesser extent. A few species have followed humans to most parts of the globe, becoming widespread and important domestic pests. The most significant pest species are discussed below.

Blattella germanica

Description

The adult *Blattella germanica* (the German cockroach) is 10–15 mm in length, with well developed wings covering the whole abdomen in the female, but leaving the terminal segments exposed in the male (Fig. 6.2). The female is stouter and more robust than the male. The colour is light to mid-brown, with two dark longitudinal dorsal bands on the prothorax (in front of the wings). In the wingless nymphal stages, these bands continue over the remainder of the thorax.

Habits

The German cockroach prefers warm, moist conditions such as occur in kitchens and restaurants. For this reason it is sometimes known as the 'Steam Fly'. It moves quickly and climbs with ease, thus it will be found in harbourages on vertical and upside-down surfaces, in cracks and crevices, behind panels and notice boards, in drawers and cupboards, inside electrical equipment, and wherever there is shelter during the hours of daylight.

At night, the insect will come out of hiding to obtain water and food. All stages will feed on any organic material available,

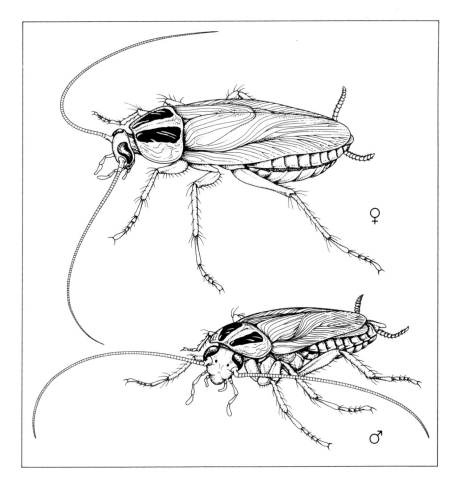

Fig. 6.2 *Blattella germanica*: female (upper) and male (lower) adults.

including refuse, debris in drains and water traps, and raw or cooked food intended for human consumption. Digestion is carried out partly by regurgitating gastric fluids from the front of the alimentary canal (the crop) on to the intended meal, which is then broken up with the mouthparts and eaten. The cockroach will defaecate indiscriminately, and the dark streaks of its faeces are a clear indication of infestation. These will appear as dark patches in heavily infested areas, and dark lines of spread faeces will show habitual pathways of the insect.

40 *Dictyoptera (cockroaches)*

Life cycle

The egg case of the German cockroach is carried by the female for about two weeks, until a few minutes before it hatches, when it is dropped at random. As the ootheca develops, it protrudes further and further from the posterior of the female and becomes very apparent. At three-week intervals the female will lay four to eight oothecae, each containing about 35 eggs, although there may be more in the earlier oothecae.

On hatching, the nymph is pale in colour but tans quickly to a pale brown. The insect will develop and increase in size through five to seven nymphal stages, over a period of some seven to nine weeks. Adults may live for four to six months, females longer than males, and reproduction will begin approximately one week after the last nymphal moult. Biological data are compared with other species and summarized in Table 6.2.

Blatta orientalis

The adult *Blatta orientalis* (the Oriental cockroach) is 20–25 mm in length and an overall dark brown to black in colour (Fig. 6.3), hence

Table 6.2 Biological data for four species of cockroach

	German cockroach	Oriental cockroach	American cockroach	Australian cockroach
Length of cockroach (mm)	10–15	20–25	30–45	30–35
Average adult life (days)				
Males	128	75–300	720	150
Females	63		630	
Number of nymphal stages				
Males	5	7	13	
Females	7	10	9	
Average nymphal development (days)				
Males	38	164	13	360
Females	63	282	5	
Number of ootheca	4–8	5–10	30	20–30
Average number of eggs per ootheca	35	15	13	24
Average incubation period of ootheca (days)	17	44	40	40
Preferred temperature range (°C)	15–35	20–29	28–33	30–35
Preferred relative humidity	80%	40–75%	80%	80%

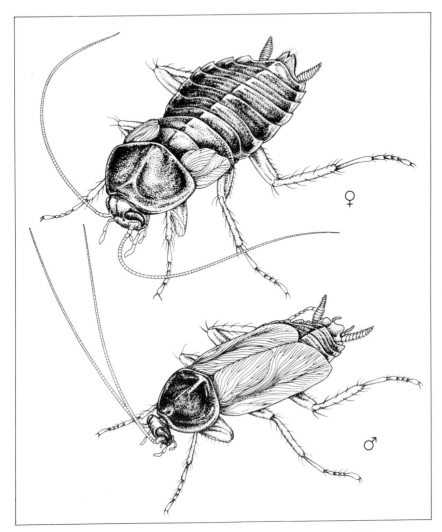

Fig. 6.3 *Blatta orientalis*: female (upper) and male (lower) adults.

the misleading common name of 'Black Beetle'. The wings are greatly reduced in the male and vestigial in the female. As well as being twice as large as the German cockroach, the Oriental cockroach is much broader and more burly.

Habits
Blatta orientalis moves more slowly than *Blattella germanica* and cannot climb efficiently since it has a very reduced pulvillus on

each foot. For this reason, it will usually only be found on horizontal surfaces or very rough vertical surfaces such as untreated brick walls. *B orientalis* prefers a cooler temperature than *B germanica* and will thus occur more frequently in cellars, basements and ducting, as well as in the slightly cooler parts of kitchens, catering areas and bathrooms. It will sometimes be found outside buildings, particularly in yards, sewers and drainage areas. It can tolerate higher temperatures in boiler rooms, provided it can obtain water – often from leaking valves or pipes. Its feeding habits are similar to *B germanica*, coming out from harbourages at night to feed, mate and defaecate. It has been reported infesting rubbish tips in cooler parts of the world.

Life cycle

The adult female Oriental cockroach will lay her first egg case some two weeks after the final nymphal moult. The eggs, usually about 15 in number, will not hatch for a further six weeks or more. Some seven to ten nymphal stages will take five to ten months to develop into the adult stages; the female passes through more nymphal stages than the male and takes the longer period. Adults will live for about six months under optimal conditions, but for considerably longer (up to two years or more) where conditions are poor and food is not readily available. Without water, however, the insect will die within a few weeks. The female will lay five to ten oothecae in her lifetime.

The reproductive capacity of the Oriental cockroach is considerably lower than that of the German cockroach. This is perhaps the main reason why it is gradually being replaced by *B germanica* as the main pest species in many temperate parts of the world. However, *B orientalis* is sometimes a more persistent pest as insecticidal treatment will not affect the unhatched eggs, necessitating at least one further treatment to kill the newly emerged nymphs (see Table 6.2).

Periplaneta americana

Periplaneta americana (the American cockroach, Plate 6) is the largest of the domestic pest cockroaches, measuring 30–45 mm in length (Fig. 6.4). Both sexes have large, well developed wings, slightly longer in the male. It is a reddish-brown colour, with prominent yellow patches on either side of the pronotum (the dorsal part of the thorax behind the head).

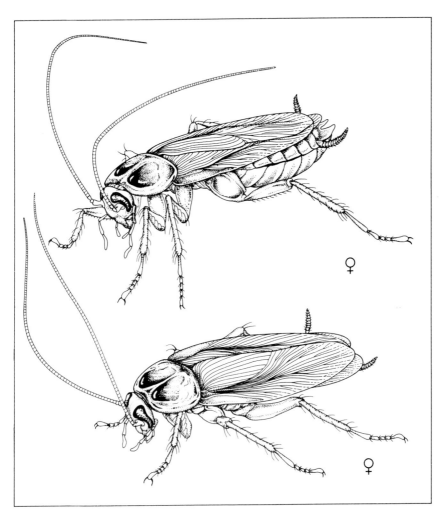

Fig. 6.4 *Periplaneta americana*: female (upper) and male (lower) adults.

The sexes can be differentiated by the appearance of the end of the abdomen which has a ventral keel in the female and a pair of ventral styles (stout bristles) in the male, in addition to the dorsal cerci of both sexes.

Habits

The American cockroach, like the German cockroach, prefers warm, moist conditions and lives indoors, in food stores and catering premises. It is often found in drains and sewers, and also commonly out-of-doors in rubbish tips and refuse areas, in warmer parts of the world. It moves rapidly, climbs efficiently and is able to fly sluggishly in a warm atmosphere, fluttering through open windows and around street lights at night.

Worldwide, *Periplaneta americana* is the most frequent and widespread cause of cockroach infestation, particularly in the tropics and subtropics.

Life cycle

P americana has by far the longest life cycle of the three important pest species. Approximately ten days after the final moult, the gravid female will lay an ootheca containing about 15 eggs on average. She takes several hours to lay an ootheca which may be seen protruding from the genital pouch, but the eggs will not hatch for some weeks. There are nine to 13 nymphal stages, fewer for the female, usually taking six to nine months to develop (although this period can be as long as two to three years). The first five nymphal stages are an almost uniform pale brown, but in succeeding stages the yellow patches on either side of the pronotum become more apparent (Plate 7).

Wing pads begin to appear in the early nymphal stages and grow more prominent with each successive moult, but wings do not develop fully until the cockroach reaches maturity. The adult life span is 21–24 months, the female producing ten to as many as 60 oothecae during this period (see Tables 6.1 and 6.2, pages 37 and 40).

Periplaneta australasiae

In terms of worldwide infestation, *Periplaneta australasiae* (the Australian cockroach) is perhaps second in importance only to *P americana*, although it is not common in temperate regions.

The Australian cockroach (Fig. 6.5) is similar in appearance, although somewhat smaller (30–35 mm) than the American cockroach. It is reddish-brown, with the yellowish lateral patches extending over the pronotum and on to the front edges of the forewings (cf. *P americana*) which are longer in the male than the female. It is able to fly actively in a warm atmosphere, and will typically be seen around street lamps at night flying into houses through open doors and windows.

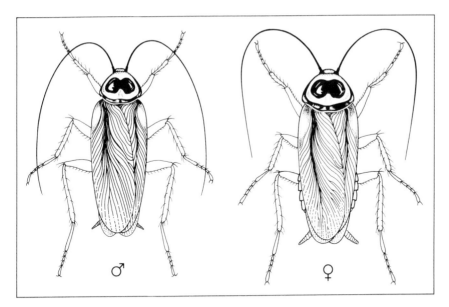

Fig. 6.5 *Periplaneta australasiae*: male (left) and female (right) adults.

Habits
P australasiae prefers a moist but somewhat warmer environment than *P americana*, and will typically be found out-of-doors in the tropics where it spreads into human habitation. In temperate regions it is found particularly in heated greenhouses, often causing damage to commercial crops.

Life cycle
This is similar to *P americana* but the duration of the adult stage is somewhat shorter. The nymphs are conspicuously marked with yellow spots on the thorax and abdomen.

Periplaneta fuliginosa

Periplaneta fuliginosa is a common pest in the southern States of North America (Fig. 6.6). The adult is 30–35 mm in length and similar in appearance to other species of *Periplaneta*, except that it is shiny and a very dark brown in colour. The wings are well developed in both sexes and cover the whole abdomen.

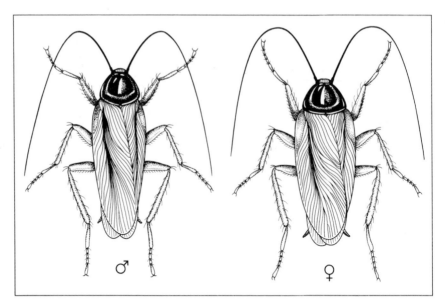

Fig. 6.6 *Periplaneta fuliginosa*: male (left) and female (right) adults.

Periplaneta brunnea

This is very similar in appearance to *P americana* (see Fig. 6.4), from which it can only be differentiated by the less conspicuous dark areas on the pronotum and the less pointed cerci in adults. Its habitat is the same as that of *P americana*.

Supella longipalpa (Supella supellectilium)

This brown banded cockroach (Fig. 6.7) is a major domestic pest in most parts of the tropics, and has spread to North America and Australia in the last 50 years. It is occasionally found in European countries.

S longipalpa is similar in size and shape to *B germanica*, being 10–15 mm in length. The wings cover the abdomen in the male, but are slightly shorter in the female which has a shorter body than the male. The colour can be very varied.

Blattella asahinai

Blattella asahinai (the Asian cockroach) is a common rural pest in many parts of South-east Asia and has recently spread to the

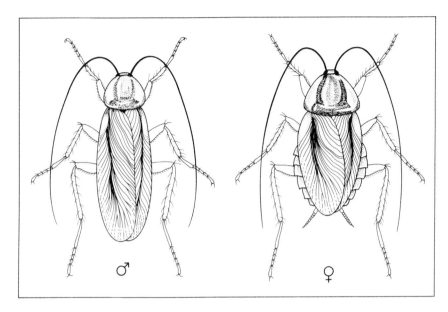

Fig. 6.7 *Supella longipalpa*: male (left) and female (right) adults.

United States of America, probably having been introduced into Florida in 1984. It is essentially an outdoor cockroach, able to fly and move rapidly over large areas. It is active from dusk to dawn, particularly at sundown, and is attracted to light and light-coloured walls, thus spreading into domestic situations where it is not upset by the presence of humans.

B asahinai is indistinguishable in appearance from the German cockroach, but it moves more rapidly and spreads more quickly over wide areas. Its rate of reproduction is faster, the female laying an ootheca containing some 40 eggs every few days, and the nymphs maturing within six to seven weeks. These factors have made the Asian cockroach an important pest species in subtropical environments.

Medical significance

Pest species of cockroach are closely associated with humans, human food and detritus. They will feed on anything available and have been shown to survive readily on human faeces, accumulated detritus in drains, used surgical swabs, sputum and other potentially infected material (Plate 8). Research has shown that the bacterial content of the cockroach gut replicates that of its environment. Thus, if potentially pathogenic material is available to the cockroach, it will take it up into its gut, but particles containing infective organisms will also adhere to its feet and body surfaces. The cockroach will then crawl over food intended for human consumption or over plates, cutlery and food preparation surfaces, leaving organisms as it progresses. While feeding, it will regurgitate fluid from its crop which will contain the organisms from the previous meal (Plate 9). As it feeds and moves around it will also leave dark spots or patches of faeces. The food, utensils and surfaces will thus become a source of infection to man (Plates 10 and 11).

Because of the nature of the organisms involved it is extremely difficult to prove that cockroaches are the prime cause of any disease outbreak. Food poisoning and other enteric infections may be passed on in a variety of ways, but circumstantial evidence and common sense indicate that where cockroaches have access to potentially infected material, and also to human food and food preparation areas, their role in the transmission of disease cannot be ignored. Cast skins may give rise to an allergic skin or respiratory response in humans. As with many insects, the presence of cockroaches may be regarded with distaste or even fear (entomophobia).

COCKROACH CONTROL

The control of a cockroach infestation necessitates an intelligent survey of the site and an appraisal of the cause of the problem. It also requires a consideration of the most effective control measures, not necessarily only those involving the use of insecticides, and an efficient control operation. This must be followed up by monitoring the result of the exercise.

Survey

This should take the form of a detailed inspection of the infested area and its surroundings, preferably carried out at night when the cockroaches will be scavenging for food. A plan of the site should be drawn and actual or potential harbourages marked on it. Sticky traps left out overnight will catch specimens which can be identified. A knockdown aerosol sprayed into cracks and crevices, behind equipment and into hollow spaces will excite cockroaches and force them out into the open where they can be collected. It is important to search thoroughly under shelving, ovens, sinks etc., therefore a torch is an essential part of an inspection kit.

A short report with the site plan should be written so that, if necessary, another operator can carry out the control measures. A full report on conditions of hygiene and housekeeping should also be included. The refuse areas is often a source of infestation, and open skips or open bins in kitchens and corridors will provide food and attract cockroaches.

The following points should also be considered:

1. Floors and walls: Are they clean and free of accumulated debris, particularly in corners and at the floor/wall junction?

2. Work surfaces, catering equipment: Are there gaps and spaces which may provide cockroach harbourages?

3. Floor/wall coverings: Are tiles cracked or broken, are there harbourages behind wall plating and panelling or under carpets, linoleum or door-mats?

4. Electrical fittings: Are cockroaches sheltering in junction boxes, switches, lighting or motor cabinets of freezers etc.?

5. Store rooms: Are cockroaches hiding under or in boxes stacked on the floor?

6. Drains: Are floor drains clean with tightly fitting covers? An infestation may well originate in a drainage system.

7. Ducting: Does this provide a harbourage and, if so, where does it lead? It is very important to carry out a three-dimensional inspection with a view to spatial control, since it is unlikely that cockroaches will be confined to one area. They will spread from a nucleus of infestation but unless treatment involves the surrounding areas, control measure may simply drive them into previously uninfested sites.

These and many other factors will constitute a good survey and with experience will become second nature to the operator. The problem often arises because architects and designers do not take the possibility of infestation into account in their plans. They tend to incorporate cosmetic panelling, false ceilings and other harbourages into the design of kitchens and restaurants, with equipment placed far enough from the wall to allow access to cockroaches but too close to allow efficient cleaning of the area.

Planning

From the survey, perhaps as part of the same visit, the most effective method of control can be determined. It is likely that the infestation has arisen because conditions of hygiene and cleanliness are below standard; it is essential that these are corrected before any control measures are carried out, since no amount of insecticide will control an infestation where housekeeping is bad. Once this has been put right, the control operation can be initiated.

Control measures

It is important that there is free access to the area to be treated, thus it is usual to treat an infestation at night or when the site is not in use. Food, utensils and other items should be removed or covered. Surfaces should be clean and the area free of unnecessary clutter.

The standard method of cockroach control is to spray a residual insecticide on to surfaces over which the insect will crawl, and to treat potential harbourages. The choice of insecticide is often predetermined by commercial policy. In a catering environment, where most surfaces are non-porous by design, an emulsion or flowable concentrate is probably preferable, although wettable powders, properly applied, can be equally effective. A wide spreading fish-tail jet should be used on the compression sprayer lance for spraying wall and floor surfaces, particularly those places which the survey has shown to be infested, for example, behind piping and in the corners which are typically used as cockroach 'motorways'. A more confined jet, often with a needle point, can be used to direct insecticide into cracks and crevices.

An electrically powered fogger may be used to cover surfaces, but this is usually not as effective as spraying since it relies on the fog finding its own way to the target. Fogs may be useful in enclosed spaces and ducting.

Where panelling is unavoidable because of design features, an insecticidal dust can be applied with a dustgun. It may be necessary to make an access hole in the panelling through which the nozzle can be pointed. This hole can be covered with a small keyhole hatch for subsequent access.

Follow up

It is very important that the residual insecticide is left in place long enough to be effective. Of course, work surfaces will have to be cleaned before they can be used for food preparation, but floors and walls should not be washed for at least 48 hours or several days, if possible. One of the disadvantages of residual insecticides is that dead and dying cockroaches will be in evidence. Catering staff should be warned of this and asked simply to collect and put them into an outside refuse bin on a daily basis. A few sticky traps, discretely and strategically placed, will give continuing evidence of the success or otherwise of the control measures. These should be inspected regularly, and follow up treatment initiated if healthy cockroaches continue to appear after about a week. It will, in any case, be necessary to carry out at least one further treatment, and this is particularly important if the infestation is due to *Blatta orientalis*, since the insecticide will not kill the eggs in the ootheca which may take up to six weeks to hatch (Plate 12).

Alternative methods to control

In some situations consideration may be given to alternative methods of control. Where the use of insecticide on surfaces is undesirable (i.e. animal rooms), poison bait may be used. This is available in capsules or containers where the bait can only be taken by the cockroach. This method is unlikely to be effective where there are other adequate sources of food.

A recent and promising advance is the use of an analogue of an insect growth regulator, hydroprene. This may be sprayed on surfaces, or incorporated into a bait. Once inside the nymphal insect hydroprene inhibits its development to the adult, and in the adult it will prevent the normal reproductive activities. Its great advantage is that it is selectively toxic to the cockroach but entirely harmless to anything else. Its disadvantage is that it will take several weeks to eradicate an infestation, producing larger nymphs which, however, do not become adult and thus will not reproduce. Hydroprene is particularly useful in long standing and deep-seated infestations where speed of control can be sacrificed for eventual success. A more rapidly acting chemical insecticide may also be incorporated into the preparation.

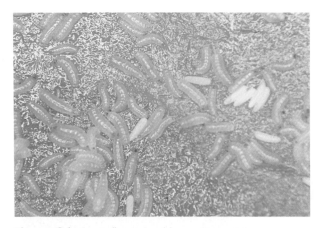

Plate 13 Calypterate fly eggs and larvae (maggots) on decomposing meat.

Plate 14 Adult flies will cause spotting with vomit drops (pale spots) and faecal deposits.

Plate 15 Typical mosquito breeding site: brackish water in tidal estuary.

Plate 16 Slow flowing water provides an ideal breeding site for some species of mosquito.

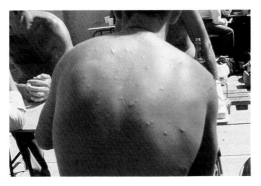

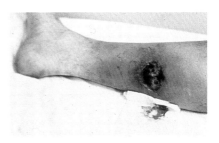

Plate 17 Typical irritating red swellings caused by reaction to mosquito bites.

Plate 18 Severe secondary infection of two mosquito bites which have been scratched.

Plate 19 Typical mosquito breeding site: woodland pool.

Plate 20 Mosquito breeding can be controlled by ensuring that water flows freely; larvicides may not always be needed.

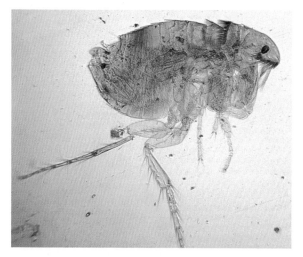

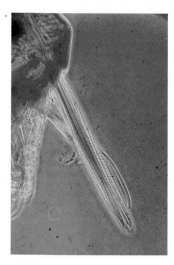

Plate 21 Adult male *Ctenocephalides felis,* the cat flea.

Plate 22 Flea mouthparts

Plate 23 Flea eggs.

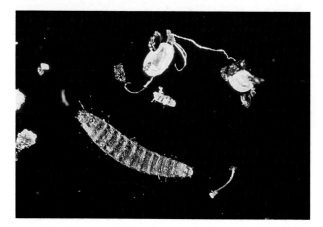

Plate 24 Debris from a flea-infested area. Note the larvae and eggs.

7

Houseflies, bluebottles and related flies

Houseflies, bluebottles and similar flies belong to an Order of the Class Insecta known as Diptera (Greek: *di* = two; *pteron* = wing). This is a large and diverse Order of insects which also includes mosquitoes and other bloodsucking midges, horse-flies and the vector of African sleeping sickness, the tsetse fly. All these insects are characterized by having only one pair of wings; the hind pair has degenerated, therefore all that remains is a pair of drumstick-like organs, the halteres, used for balance in flight.

Diptera are only able to take fluid food, which in the case of bloodsucking flies is obtained by injecting the piercing mouthparts (proboscis) into living tissue. In other flies, food is liquidized externally by puddling it with spongy mouthparts in digestive fluid regurgitated from the foregut (crop).

All Diptera go through a complete metamorphosis in their life cycle, developing from the egg through a number of larval stages to the pupa from which the adult emerges. The larva, which is the feeding and growing stage, is typically found in a completely different environment from the adult, although the adult will be associated with the larval environment when mating and laying eggs (Plate 13).

A large group within the Diptera, sometimes known as the calypterate flies (because the halteres are shielded from above by saucer-like processes known as calypters), includes houseflies (*Musca* species), bluebottles (*Calliphora* species), greenbottles (*Lucilia* species), lesser houseflies (*Fannia* species) and grey fleshflies (*Sarcophaga* and *Wohlfahrtia* species). It is those species which are closely associated with humans and have adapted to the human domestic environment. They are of public health importance as pests and potential carriers of disease organisms.

HOUSEFLY

This common name is applied to flies within the *Musca domestica* complex in most parts of the world, both temperate and tropical, and also to flies in the *Musca sorbens* complex in the Old World tropics and subtropics, including Australia. They are the flies which have become most closely associated with humans, and

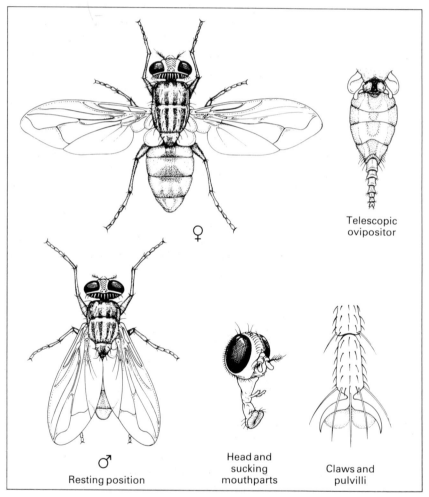

Fig. 7.1 *Musca domestica*, the housefly. The female is shown, together with the telescopic ovipositor (upper), as well as the male, both in their resting positions. The male head and sucking mouthparts, claws and pulvilli are also depicted (lower).

they will be used as a comparative example for all domestic pest flies.

The housefly is a broad and burly insect, with a well differentiated head, thorax and abdomen and two broad wings (Fig. 7.1). In length it ranges between 6–9 mm with a spread wingspan of 13–15 mm. A large proportion of the upper head surface is covered with optical cells making up the pair of compound eyes which give the fly good all-round vision. Between the eyes there is a pair of short sausage-shaped antennae, and below these the retractible mouthparts (proboscis) terminate in a spongy pad. The flat base of the pad is covered in small channels which connect to the hollow proboscis and hence to the mouth and alimentary canal. The thorax is robust and grey in colour, with four broad and dark dorsal stripes running longitudinally. Each of the six legs ends in a pair of claws and a pair of pads (pulvilli) covered in minute hairs. The wings are attached to the middle segment of the three-segmented thorax and have a characteristic pattern made by the veins (venation). These are hollow tubes which support the wing, continuous with the body cavity and filled with body fluid. From the third (hindmost) thoracic segment come the halteres, covered from above by the calypters (see Fig. 7.1).

The abdomen has no appendages; it is grey and black in the male but a more prominent yellow and black in the female, which also has a telescopic portion (the ovipositor) at the end of the abdomen through which she lays her eggs (Fig. 7.2).

Life cycle

The life cycle is illustrated in Figure 7.2. The larval stages are associated with decomposing organic matter of all types, thus the female will lay a batch of eggs, numbering about a hundred, on rotting dustbin refuse and rubbish, decomposing and even fresh food, dead animals and other organic material (see Plate 13). She will lay six to eight batches of eggs after only one mating, storing the sperm in the spermatheca, and may live for several weeks. The banana-shaped eggs, usually laid in a mass, are about 1 mm in length and creamy white in colour. They hatch within 12 hours and typical maggot-shaped larvae emerge. The larva is whitish, with a pointed head at the top of which are dark mouthparts for chewing the food source using regurgitated fluid to digest it. The body broadens posteriorly to a flattened plate which has a pair of spiracles.

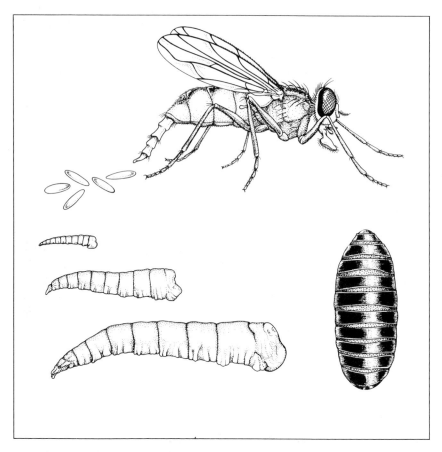

Fig. 7.2 The female housefly, side view. The ovipositor is seen at the end of the abdomen, through which she lays her eggs. The life cycle is also depicted: eggs, larval stages and pupa to the adult.

The larva will feed voraciously, usually in a sheltered part of the food source, and will crawl back into cover if exposed to light. It increases considerably in size, passing through three stages (i.e. moulting twice) over a period of about seven days, before it is fully grown and measuring 10–15 mm in length. The mature larva will crawl to a drier and more secluded environment, often burying itself in the substrate. Unlike most Diptera it does not moult but uses its third stage larval skin in which to pupate (this is known as a puparium rather than a pupa). The pupal stage is hard, dark brown to black in colour and lozenge-shaped. It does not feed or move at all. After a further three to five days the adult fly will emerge from the pupal case.

The periods of development (12 hours for the egg to hatch, seven days for the larva and three to five days for the pupal stage) may be considerably longer in colder or adverse conditions, particularly in the larval stage which may last for three to four weeks. Temperature is a very crucial factor. For example, at 16°C the immature cycle is about seven weeks, whereas at 35°C it may only be one week.

Habits

Adult flies will be attracted to decomposing and other organic matter on which the females will lay their eggs. Males will look for females with which to mate. While in this environment, both sexes will feed by regurgitating fluid from the crop, puddling it on the organic matter with their sponge-like mouthparts and then sucking the liquidized food up the proboscis to the gut. Chemical receptors, particularly in the antennae, will indicate the presence of organic material to the adult fly, and sex attractant pheromones will also play a part in bringing the males and females together.

Medical significance

Houseflies have long been regarded as potential carriers of disease, mainly of the enteric type, particularly in the tropics and subtropics where they are more likely to have access to a source of infection. When the fly feeds, perhaps on infected human faeces, it takes the infective organisms into its gut. Particles adhere to its bristles and body surfaces, and are taken up by the tiny hairs on its foot pads. At a subsequent feed, perhaps on food prepared for human consumption, the fly will go through its feeding process, regurgitating fluid over the food, which will contain the organisms from a previous meal. It will deposit particles from its body while it preens itself, or from its feet as it walks over the food. It will also defaecate indiscriminately, contaminating surfaces both during a meal and afterwards while resting (Plate 14). In this way disease organisms are carried by the fly in a purely mechanical manner from an infected source to humans. The process is very similar to that performed by cockroaches. However, being able to fly several kilometres, flies can transport infective organisms with ease.

In tropical areas adult flies will be present throughout the year, but in temperate regions, where flies and cockroaches may also be contributory to disease epidemiology, flies are only present during the warmer parts of the year and cockroaches may be more significant as a health hazard.

The larval stages of some flies may cause a condition known as **myiasis** when they infect sores or wounds in human tissue, mistaking it for decomposing organic matter, which of course it may be.

Control

Houseflies which occur in sufficient numbers to cause a pest problem are almost certainly being attracted to the site because of a breakdown in standards of hygiene. The initial survey will give a good indication of this. The cause is likely to be a badly managed refuse area, blocked or dirty drains, open rubbish containers or generally dirty conditions in which decomposing organic debris accumulates. These conditions are often accompanied by a poor standard of housekeeping and food preparation, and it is here that the danger of contamination and disease becomes a real threat.

Occasionally, the presence of flies may be due to external causes such as a nearby farm or cattle in an adjacent field, and sometimes the problem can be traced to a very localized source such as a dead bird or rodent in a blocked fireplace or even floor mops in which the core is decomposing, both of which provide breeding sites for flies. Thus the most important aspect of any fly control operation is to trace the cause of the problem and correct it. Once acceptable standards of hygiene and food preparation have been achieved, control or preventive measures can be undertaken.

Insecticidal control
Adult flies rest on walls and ceilings. This habit can be utilized by spraying such surfaces with a residual insecticide, using a compression sprayer fitted with a fish-tail jet. A wettable powder or an emulsion/flowable concentrate may be used, depending on the nature (porous or otherwise) or the surface to be treated. A knockdown aerosol can be used to rid a room temporarily of flies, but this is not an effective method of control, particularly since the affected fly will move in an uncontrolled manner which may result in contamination of food with its dead body. Aerosols should never be used near food or utensils.

Fly proofing

Windows of food preparation areas may be fitted with fly screens to prevent the entry of flying insects. However, the design should be such that it allows the window to be opened, and the screen must be cleaned regularly. Similar screens may be fitted in doorways and should include a spring return to keep the door closed. Fly screens are particularly useful in rural areas and where control of potential fly breeding sites in the surrounding area is not possible.

Ultraviolet (UV) fly traps

These flying insect killers (EFKs) are described on page 21. It is important to ensure that the correct capacity of trap is fitted, and that it is sited away from competing daylight and fluorescent-tube lighting. A dark corner is the most effective site. EFKs are only contributory to fly control; they are most effective when all other light is excluded, i.e. at night, but houseflies will be unlikely to fly under these conditions. Night-flying insects, such as moths, will often be caught. Experiments have shown that in daylight only about one in five flies in a room will be trapped in an EFK, but this is still acceptable. The tray at the base of the trap must be cleaned regularly, having first switched off the electricity supply. Some traps are designed to be wall mounted, others to be suspended in the middle of the room.

BLUEBOTTLE (*CALLIPHORA* SPECIES)

This species tends to breed more commonly on dead animals and fish, and will fly indoors with a typically loud and apparently uncontrolled flight, settling on food and waste matter. For this reason the bluebottle is a hazard to health and will cause contamination by its feeding habits.

Calliphora is a large, robust fly 10–15 mm in length, with a wing span of up to 25 mm, shiny blue in colour and covered in stout dark bristles (Fig. 7.3). A useful diagnostic characteristic is the presence of small dark hairs on its calypters which have a light border.

If large numbers of bluebottles occur over a short period, it is likely that they have emerged from one source such as a dead animal in a fireplace or other enclosed area. The odour of the decomposing animal may be apparent. The source of infestation should be found and removed before the next generation of flies lays eggs on it, although it is likely that the earlier maggots will

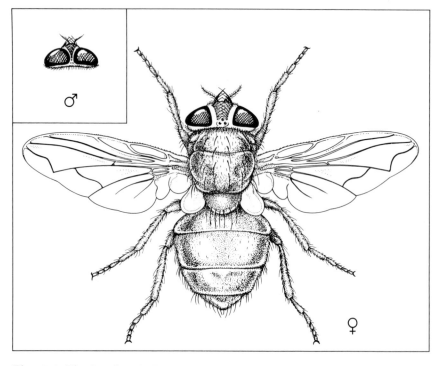

Fig. 7.3 Bluebottle, *Calliphora* species, seen from the top. The inset diagram shows the shape of the eyes in the male, which is the main external distinguishing feature.

have consumed all the available nutriment and no further infestation will occur.

GREENBOTTLE (*LUCILIA* SPECIES)

These flies are a shiny green, about 10 mm long, less bristly than the bluebottle and with bare calypters (Fig. 7.4). Their habits are in general similar to the bluebottle.

LESSER HOUSEFLIES (*FANNIA* SPECIES)

These flies are similar in appearance to *Musca domestica*, although somewhat smaller and more slender (Fig. 7.5). The adults will typically fly in a leisurely manner around objects suspended from

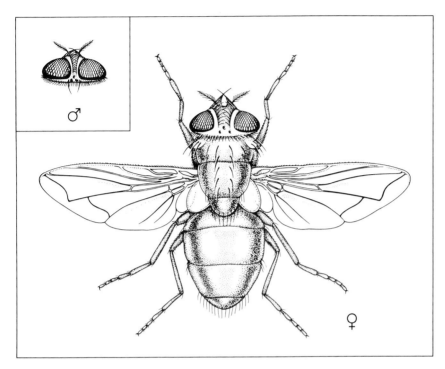

Fig. 7.4 Greenbottle, *Lucilia* species. The inset diagram shows the shape of the eyes in the male, which is the main external distinguishing feature.

the ceiling, particularly light pendants, and will settle on ceilings and walls. The life cycle is similar to that of the housefly, except that the larva is often associated with urine-soaked material (human or animal) and has adapted to this by developing long spines on its body. Control measures used against *Musca domestica* will be effective against all species of domestic fly pests.

Cluster flies

Some species will occasionally cause concern by congregating in large numbers on walls or inside windows. This is a seasonal phenomenon and is caused by flies moving to an enclosed area such as a loft space to hibernate to the autumn, or leaving hibernation in the spring. Cluster flies breed in animal dung or earthworms. In the autumn they will aggregate on sunlit walls,

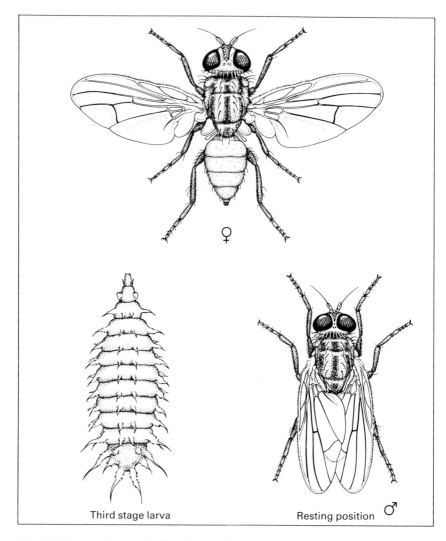

Fig. 7.5 Lesser housefly *Fannia* species.

crawling into warmer, more sheltered places at night, eventually hibernating for several months.

In the spring, or occasionally on warmer late winter days, the flies may emerge from hibernation. They will cluster in large numbers on window panes, crawling sluggishly in an attempt to reach the open air. Three species of cluster fly occur commonly,

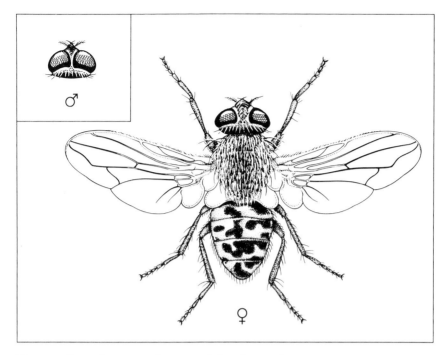

Fig. 7.6 *Dasyphora cyanella*, one of the cluster fly species.

Musca autumnalis, similar in size and appearance to the housefly; *Pollenia rudis*, somewhat larger and a dull grey/brown with wings folded scissor-like over the abdomen; and *Dasyphora cyanella*, about the same size as the housefly but a shiny green/blue colour (Fig. 7.6).

A knockdown aerosol insecticide may be used to kill the flies. As a deterrent to infestation, sunlit walls may be sprayed in the early autumn with a residual insecticidal wettable powder, and loft spaces where flies hibernate may be similarly treated.

FRUIT FLIES

These are small (3 mm in length) burly flies, yellow/brown in colour, belonging to the genus *Drosophila* (Fig. 7.7). Adults are typically found flying with a hovering ponderous flight in breweries, fruit, vegetable and wine stores, and refuse areas, where they are attracted by fermenting organic matter, vinegar and other vapours. They may live for two to three weeks at room

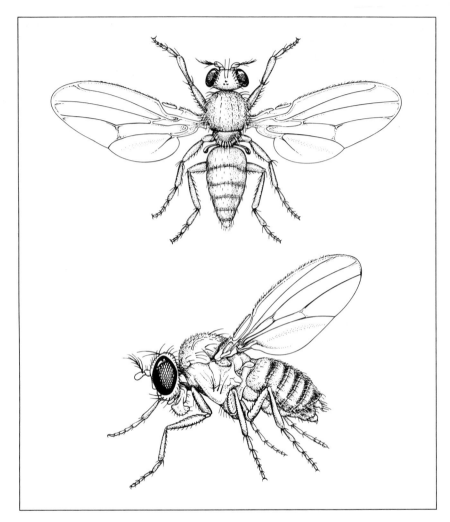

Fig. 7.7 *Drosophila*, the fruit fly.

temperature (20°C). The maggot-like larvae feed in decaying fruit and material impregnated with fermenting fluids. Larval development takes about two weeks.

Fruit flies occurring in large numbers may cause a nuisance by contaminating food and beverages. The most satisfactory method of control is to remove any attractive substance, confining it to a closed refuse area, and to avoid spillage from machines dispensing sweet drinks. Bottle stores should be discretely sited and fly-proofed, if possible, to avoid access of fruit flies to dregs of beverages. Fruit and vegetables should be stored in a cool environment and over-ripe items discarded. Ultraviolet fly traps are moderately effective. An aerosol may be used to remove flies in an enclosed area.

8

Mosquitoes

Mosquitoes belong to the Order Diptera and hence have only one pair of wings and a pair of halteres (see page 53). They can only take fluid food in the form of nectar and plant exudates and, significantly in the female only, in the form of blood. There are approximately 4000 species of mosquitoes distributed throughout most parts of the world, with about 30 species in the British Isles.

The mosquito is a slender insect with narrow wings and long thin legs (Fig. 8.1). The length from the tip of the proboscis to the end of the abdomen is 7–15 mm, depending on the species, and this is similar to the wingspan for that particular species. The head has two large compound eyes. A long proboscis extends forwards and contains the mouthparts; on either side of the proboscis are the paired palps (Fig. 8.2). The appearance of the palps is helpful in differentiating the two main groups of pest mosquito, the anophelines and the culicines (see Fig. 8.2). Outside the palps, and arising just below the eyes, are the pair of antennae which are heavily covered in long hairs in the male mosquito and sparsely haired in the female. This is an important feature since it differentiates the blood-sucking female from the non-biting male.

The thorax holds the three pairs of long slender legs, as well as a pair of long narrow wings with a characteristic venation common to all mosquitoes (Fig. 8.3). The wings are covered in flattened hairs or scales which may occur in dark patches, another differentiating feature. The abdomen is conspicuously segmented and may have contrasting bands of scales on each segment.

LIFE CYCLE

The mosquito, in common with all Diptera, exhibits a complete metamorphosis in its life cycle (Fig. 8.4). The immature stages are

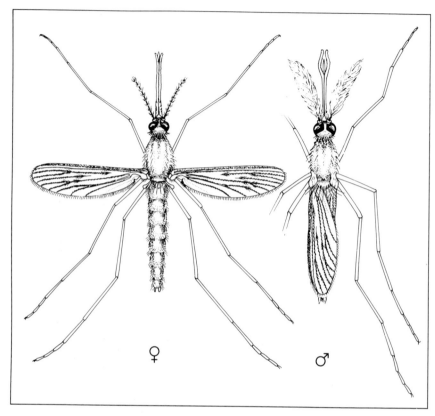

Fig. 8.1 Typical mosquito, viewed from the top. Male (right) and female (left) examples.

always closely associated with water, ranging from small collections in old cans on rubbish tips to the edges of slow-flowing rivers (Plates 15 and 16). The eggs will be laid by the gravid female on the surface of water in groups, each egg having a pair of lateral air floats (anophelines), or in a raft formation (some culicines). Sometimes eggs are laid in groups above the surface of water or in a hollow or container which is flooded by rain or melting ice (some culicines). The eggs hatch within a few hours of being laid (or being covered in water), and a minute worm-like larval stage will emerge. There are four larval stages which will feed voraciously on microorganisms in the water or on the surface.

The larva obtains oxygen by coming up to the surface, suspended there by surface tension and taking in air through a pair

ANOPHELINE	CULICINE

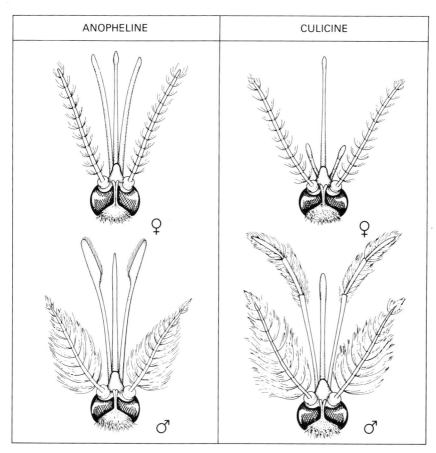

Fig. 8.2 Female and male Anopheline and Culicine heads, showing eyes, antennae and proboscis.

of spiracles at its hind end. In anophelines, these spiracles are flush with the dorsal surface, hence the larva lies parallel to the surface when respiring and will often feed in this position (see Fig. 8.4). In culicines, the spiracles are situated on the end of a tube or siphon, hence the larva will hang from the surface by the tip of the siphon, typically feeding deeper in the water. When the fourth-stage larva is fully fed and mature, it will moult to form a comma-shaped pupa. This does not feed, but unlike most insect pupae it is able to move around rapidly in the water, using paired paddles at the end of the abdomen which hangs down from the

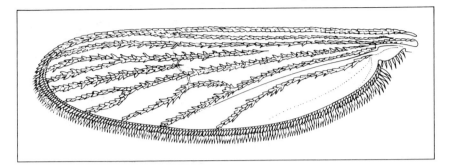

Fig. 8.3 Characteristic wing venation, common to all mosquitoes.

fused bulk of the head and thorax (cephalothorax). The pupa will come to the water surface to obtain air through a pair of 'trumpets' atached to the thoracic spiracles. When the adult is fully formed in the pupal case, the pupa comes to the surface, splits across the top and the adult emerges, standing on the water surface while the exoskeleton hardens and the wings are opened out (see Fig. 8.4).

In a breeding site, males will usually emerge first and swarm above the water. Mating will take place as soon as the females emerge. The male sperm is stored by the female in her spermatheca and will be used to fertilize eggs as they pass down her oviduct. She may lay up to six batches of eggs but will only mate once during her lifetime. However, before she can lay viable eggs she will, in most species, need to take a blood meal from a mammal or bird (some of the amino acids in the blood are needed to develop the eggs). She is attracted to a host by a number of stimuli, particularly heat and exhaled carbon dioxide.

Having found a host she will settle and probe with her proboscis to locate a blood vessel, whereupon she will typically inject a small amount of anticoagulant saliva into the bite puncture to prevent the blood from clotting. It is the reaction of the host's antibodies to this attack which causes the redness, swelling and irritation at the site of the bite. If the host has not developed the necessary antibodies little or no reaction will occur, although antibodies will be formed within a few hours or days of being bitten. This is why

Fig. 8.4 Anopheline and Culicine life cycles. From the eggs to the larval stages, to the pupa and to the adult.

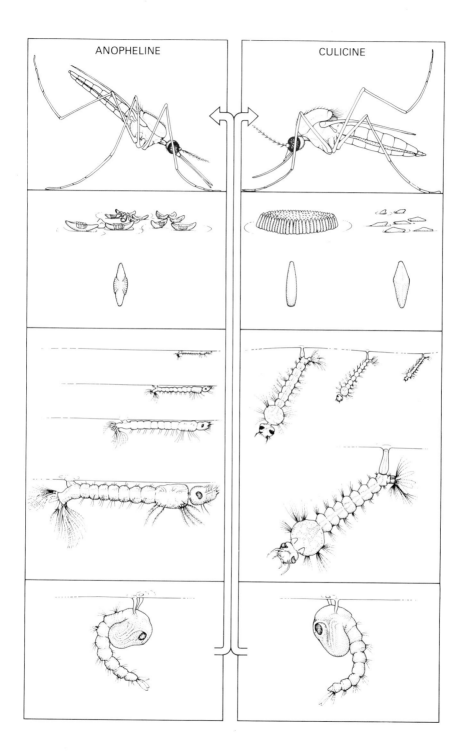

ANOPHELINE

CULICINE

appear not to be bitten by mosquitoes – it is simply that they are not reacting.

The length of life cycle is extremely varied and will depend a great deal on the geographical location and local climatic conditions. Some tropical species will go through many generations within a year; the larval and pupal stages may develop in seven to ten days, and the adults may live only two to three weeks. In temperate regions, there may only be one generation in a year and hibernation may take place at any stage depending on the species, so that egg, larval or adult stages could last many weeks.

HABITS

Female mosquitoes will typically feed at night. Many species are most active at dusk and dawn, although some, particularly woodland species, will feed during the day. Male mosquitoes are unable to pierce animal tissue because the internal mouthparts within the proboscis are too short. The females of many species will feed on humans, given the opportunity. Some species will prefer human blood and may rest in houses before or after a bloodmeal, or may only enter houses to feed. Many species will only feed on humans out-of-doors.

MEDICAL SIGNIFICANCE

In the tropics and subtropics the female mosquito is without doubt the most important vector of human disease, carrying malaria, filariasis, and a large range of virus diseases such as yellow fever, dengue fever and forms of encephalitis. A number of these viruses also occur in the warmer, temperate zones, and until relatively recent times malaria was common in many cooler parts of the world. It is only through their blood-sucking habits that mosquitoes can transmit disease, and even where disease does not occur this habit can give rise to considerable discomfort and distress (Plates 17 and 18).

Table 8.1 shows the major diseases transmitted by the anopheline and culicine mosquitoes.

CONTROL MEASURES

Effective control of mosquitoes requires a detailed knowledge of the particular species involved. Thus the assistance of a specialist

Table 8.1 Diseases transmitted by mosquitoes

Anopheline	*Culicine*
Malaria	Filiariasis
Filariasis	Many Arboviruses, including
	Yellow Fever
	Dengue Fever
Some Arboviruses	Japanese Encephalitis

entomologist may well be invaluable in identifying the species and advising on its habits. Since mosquitoes have a complete metamorphosis in their life cycle, there are two completely separate environments and phases in which the pest problem can be controlled, namely, the immature breeding sites and the adult resting places. These will be discussed in turn.

Larval control

If a mosquito pest problem exists it will be emanating from breeding sites nearby, no further than one or two kilometres distant and probably much closer, although adult mosquitoes have been known to fly up to five kilometres. Thus, a survey should be made of the surrounding area and likely collections of water investigated. Larvae and pupae can be collected by taking samples from the edge of the water; a soup ladle is a very useful piece of equipment for this. The larvae can be identified by a specialist or allowed to mature to the adult stage for this purpose. Once the specimens are identified and the health hazard confirmed, a control programme can be initiated.

As with all control measures, non-insecticidal methods should first be considered. It is often possible to remove the breeding sites by clearing away containers and other refuse which hold water, or by draining or in-filling depressions and puddles. Sluggish streams and gulleys can be channelled so that the water flows too quickly to allow mosquito larvae to survive (Plates 19 and 20). In developing countries the need to control mosquitoes is often paramount because of their role in the transmission of disease. However, in developed countries ecological considerations must be taken into account, and the draining of mosquito breeding sites may have a significant effect on the natural environment. There is always a difficult balance to be maintained between the need to control and the need to preserve.

Larviciding
Mosquito larvae may be killed by adding material to the surface of the water to reduce the surface tension, thus preventing the larvae from obtaining oxygen. This can be achieved by applying a light oil, prepared commercially for this purpose, incorporating a spreading agent and emulsifier, to the water surface, using a compression sprayer. In an emergency a light diesel oil can be used. More recently, a fat derivative known as lecithin has become available. This has the ability to spread rapidly over the water surface until it forms a layer only one cell thick (a monolayer), which acts in the same way as an oil in reducing surface tension. Under ideal conditions these methods may be effective, but they have disadvantages: they may not be ecologically acceptable and they rely on the formation of a continuous layer over the water surface which may be broken by vegetation, wind and water currents.

Insecticidal larvicides may be used under certain environmental conditions. These are usually flowable concentrates (see page 15) of active ingredients such as pirimiphos-methyl, chlorpyrifos, temephos or permethrin. They are applied to the breeding site through a compression sprayer, diluted according to the label instruction. However, at the time of writing these products do not have HSE approval for use in mosquito control in Britain. The application of biological methods of control is becoming more important in developed countries, in particular the bacterium *Bacillus thuringiensis israelensis* (Bti) and the insect growth regulator methoprene.

Bti, when applied to mosquito breeding sites, produces a toxin which kill mosquito larvae by causing their gut to disintegrate when they imbibe it. It can be applied as a liquid or powder, or may be incorporated in a monolayer (see above). It is most effective when taken up by the first and second stage larvae, hence the time of treatment is critical and sometimes difficult to judge. The main disadvantage of Bti is that it is only effective for 24–48 hours after application, but it is specifically toxic to mosquitoes and a few other groups (Chironomids and Dixids) living in the same environment.

Methoprene is similarly selective but acts in a different manner, since it is a synthetic analogue of the juvenile hormone produced by the earlier immature stages of the mosquito. Moulting in the immature stages is governed by a balance between two hormones produced by the larva: the moulting hormone present throughout the cycle, and the juvenile hormone produced in increasingly smaller amounts as the larva develops and disappearing at pupation. If the synthetic analogue is added to the water in which larvae are developing and feeding, its presence will inhibit moulting and the adult insect will not emerge. Methoprene may be applied through a pressure sprayer as a flowable concentrate, in slow-release blocks or mixed with sand. Only a very small amount is needed (the recommended dose is 216 ml active ingredient per hectare), and it remains effective for up to 28 days at 15°C (rather less at higher temperatures).

Control of a mosquito pest problem in its immature stages is to be recommended since it removes the infestation at its source and prevents further occurrence. However, it will also be necessary to control the adult mosquitoes which actually cause the health hazard and give rise to further generations of adults from untreated breeding sites.

Adult mosquito control

The collection of specimens is again important since identification of a mosquito species will indicate the most effective control measures for that particular species. Mosquitoes will often be found cohabiting with non-biting midges (Chironomids, Dixids) which may occur in large numbers, giving the impression of a much more severe problem than actually exists. These midges can be readily distinguished from mosquitoes by the absence of a long forwardly projecting proboscis. Mosquitoes which are causing the problem can be collected in 3 × 1 inch glass or plastic tubes while resting on walls of houses, or with the aid of a suction tube or 'pooter'. Absolute evidence that the mosquito is human-biting can be obtained if it is actually collected while feeding, but this should only be done if there is no danger of disease transmission.

Adult mosquitoes can be killed by using either knockdown or residual insecticides. A flying insect killer aerosol can be used in a confined space, by closing windows and doors, using the aerosol as directed and leaving the room closed for 15 minutes. Mosquitoes flying out-of-doors can be controlled by fogging with a swingfog or similar piece of equipment, or by spraying a knockdown insecticide at ultra-low volume in the atmosphere through which the mosquitoes are flying. Only insecticides with label approval for this purpose should be used, the recommended protective clothing must be worn and direct contamination of the public avoided.

Control should be undertaken when the mosquitoes are most active, usually at dusk and dawn. The insecticide will only be effective if mosquitoes actually fly through the fog, since there is little or no residual effect. Residual insecticides can, however, be used effectively by spraying them over surfaces where mosquitoes will rest (walls, ceilings, eaves of buildings etc). This is carried out using a compression sprayer. It may be necessary to treat buildings inside as well as outside, depending on the habits of the species concerned. External walls may require frequent treatment if rain washes off the insecticide, but the sheltered parts of the eaves and roof spaces will provide common mosquito resting places.

Personal protection

A great deal can be done to avoid being bitten by mosquitoes and other blood-sucking flies. Sleeping accommodation can be fitted with mosquito proofing over the windows and doors, and mosquito bed-nets can be used. These should be impregnated with a suitable insecticide approved for this purpose (i.e. permethrin in the form of Peripel). This will dissuade smaller midges, sandflies etc. from entering through the mesh, and will also keep mosquitoes out if the net is damaged or not properly tucked in.

Insect repellents can be applied to exposed parts of the body, but legs and arms should be covered with clothing as much as possible after dusk. Mosquito coils, which give off a vapour of insecticide when burnt, are effective if placed under a table to prevent legs being bitten, and small electrically powered 'hot plates' are recommended for use in sleeping quarters see page 19. Electronic (ultrasonic) bleepers are completely useless.

9

Fleas

Fleas make up a separate Order of insects, the Siphonaptera, containing some 3000 species worldwide. They are all blood-sucking, temporary ectoparasites of warm-blooded animals, mainly mammals, but a few will feed on birds. Only a small proportion will attack humans. Fleas, like bedbugs, are comparatively host-specific, but will often feed readily on other animals if their preferred host is not available.

Fleas are flattened from side to side (laterally, as opposed to dorsoventrally in most insects); this is a useful adaptation to enable them to move easily through the hairs or feathers of their host. Their length ranges between 1–8 mm; they are oval in shape (Fig. 9.1) and light to dark brown in colour. The small head has a proboscis that projects downwards (Plate 22) and small antennae recessed into grooves. Most fleas have a pair of small simple eyes (ocelli), although some are blind, usually those which live on hosts with underground burrows. Fleas are secondarily wingless, but have powerful legs adapted for jumping and can leap 10–15 cm, the equivalent of a hundred or more metres for humans. The abdomen is the bulkiest part of the body and is conspicuously segmented. The ending is rounded in the female, whereas in the male the genitalia are apparent.

LIFE CYCLE

The life cycle is one of complete metamorphosis (Fig. 9.2). It typically takes place in the resting place of the host, in the nest, burrow or other habitation. The eggs are comparatively large, 0.5 mm in length and oval or round in shape (Plate 23). They are pearly white, and are laid by the gravid female in the host's resting place or sometimes on the host itself, from where they fall to the

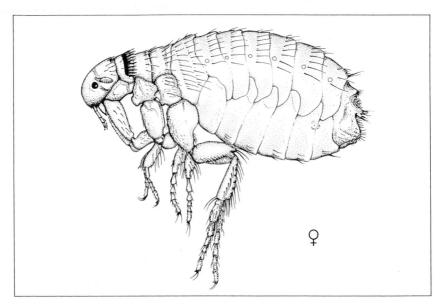

Fig. 9.1 Typical flea (female). Side view.

ground. They have a slightly sticky coating which attracts debris from the habitat, thus camouflaging their appearance. The female flea may live for several months and will lay 20–30 eggs per day.

From the egg, which hatches about a week after being laid, emerges a maggot-like larva with a small, usually dark head capsule containing chewing mouthparts and short antennae. The larva is legless and is covered in long body hairs with two small processes (anal struts) at the posterior end; it moves rapidly in search of food. Adult fleas in the habitat will take more blood than they require from the host. This is partly digested and defaecated into the habitat where it dries and provides nutriment for the larval stages – an unusual form of parental care in the insect world (Plate 25). The larvae also feed on other organic debris. After four stages or instars, lasting one to three weeks, the mature larva spins a cocoon around itself, inside which it pupates. On this cocoon adhere particles from the larval environment.

The adult will break out of the pupal case within a week or two, but will remain inside the cocoon until it senses the presence of a potential bloodmeal to ensure its survival. It may stay protected in this way for up to a year. Thus, a heavy flea infestation may appear in a building or room which has been unoccupied for some time.

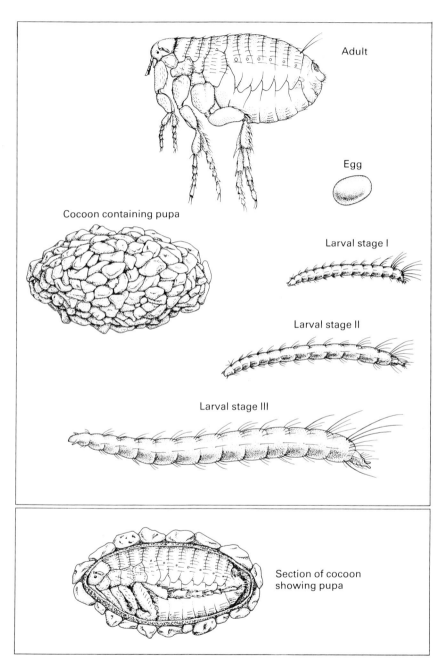

Adult

Egg

Cocoon containing pupa

Larval stage I

Larval stage II

Larval stage III

Section of cocoon
showing pupa

Fig. 9.2 Life cycle of the flea.

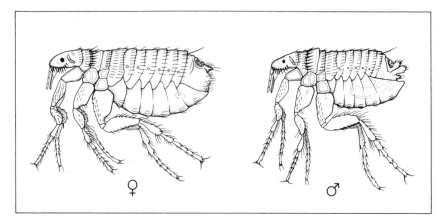

Fig. 9.3 *Ctenocephalides felis*, the cat flea. Male and female side views.

Both males and females require blood for nutrition and feed on nothing else. The female also requires blood from her preferred host in order to lay viable eggs.

HABITS OF HUMAN-BITING FLEAS

A number of fleas will feed on humans. Humans are the preferred host of *Pulex irritans*, but it will feed readily on pigs and breeds rapidly in pigsties. It will also feed on other animals, but does not produce viable eggs. The human flea lives in cooler and damper

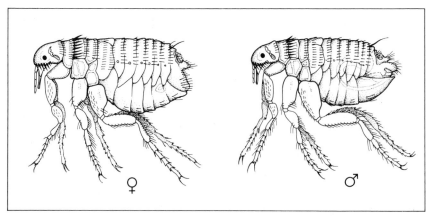

Fig. 9.4 *Ctenocephalides canis*, the dog flea. Male and female side views.

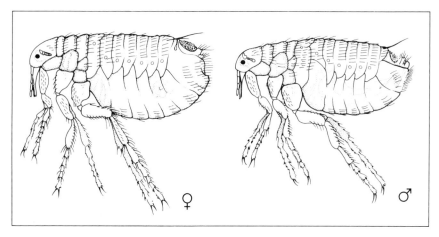

Fig. 9.5 *Xenopsylla*, the tropical rat flea. Male and female side views.

human habitation, and for this reason it is becoming much less common in developed countries and dwellings of better standards. The cat flea *Ctenocephalides felis* (Fig. 9.3; also see Plate 21) while preferring the blood of domestic cats and other members of the cat family, will readily feed on humans in the domestic environment, although viable eggs are not usually produced.

The cat flea will also feed on dogs and small mammals such as rodents, while the dog flea *Ctenocephalides canis* (Fig. 9.4) will

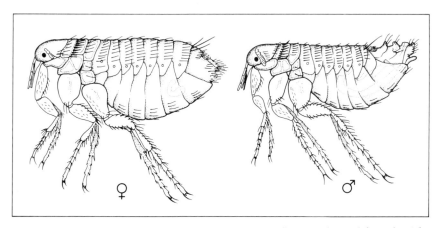

Fig. 9.6 *Nosopsyllus fasciatus*, the European rat flea. Male and female side views.

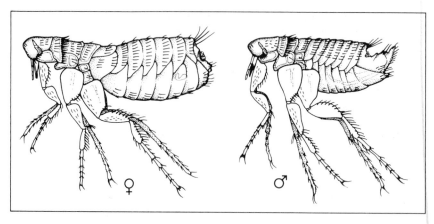

Fig. 9.7 *Leptopsylla segnis*, the mouse flea. Male and female side views.

feed on cats although preferring dogs, foxes etc. Humans are sometimes attacked by rodent fleas, particularly the tropical rat fleas in the genus *Xenopsylla* (Fig. 9.5) which are the vector of human bubonic plague. The European rat flea *Nosopsyllus fasciatus* (Fig. 9.6), thought to have been the carrier of the Black Death, will also bite, as will some of the bird fleas in the genus *Ceratophyllus*, and rarely the mouse flea *Leptopsylla segnis* (Fig. 9.7).

Fleas tend to bite humans on the nearest available site, thus bites on the lower legs are indicative of a flea infestation.

DIFFERENTIATION OF ADULT HUMAN-BITING FLEAS (Table 9.1)

A diagnostic Table is shown at Table 7. The important differentiating features are the presence or absence of:

1. The genal comb, a row of stout bristles on either side of head.

2. The thoracic comb, a row of similar bristles pointing backwards from the front of the thorax.

3. The mesothoracic suture, a split in the lower middle segment of the thorax.

4. An eye on either side of the head.

Table 9.1 Distinguishing features of medically important fleas

	Genal comb	Thoracic comb	Mesothoracic suture	Eyes
Pulex irritans	No	No	No	Yes
Ctenocephalides felis/canis	Yes	Yes	No	Yes
Nosopsyllus fasciatus	No	Yes	No	Yes
Xenopsylla species	No	No	No	Yes
Ceratophyllus species	No	Yes	No	Yes
Leptosylla segnis	Yes	Yes	Yes	No

CONTROL MEASURES

All stages of the flea will be found in the habitat of the host, thus it is this area which requires treatment (Plate 24). For every flea found on the host animal there will probably be a hundred or more in the burrow, nest or cat basket, hence the effectiveness of insecticidal collars on cats and dogs is very limited. Domestic infestations in Britain are commonly caused by the cat flea. Improved conditions of housing and the use of vacuum cleaners have led to the almost total demise of the human flea, whereas warmer, drier conditions, fitted carpets and pet cats and dogs are ideal for cat fleas. Hygiene is again paramount; the infested area should first be vacuumed and then an insecticidal dust or wettable powder, approved for this purpose, should be applied, particularly to the edges of carpets at the floor/wall join. Upholstered furniture should be vacuumed and similarly treated, taking care to treat the space under the cushions of armchairs where debris has collected. The bedding of cat or dog should be replaced or thoroughly washed.

Before using a wettable powder through a compression sprayer, it is wise to spray a small amount on to the upholstery in a part which does not show, to ensure that the colour does not run. Most wettable powders do not damage surfaces, whereas, because of the nature of the carrier, many emulsion concentrates will cause marking. The insect growth regulator methroprene is effective against particularly persistent flea infestations, preventing the development of larvae to the pupal and adult stage. It is applied in diluted liquid form through a compression sprayer. All liquid insecticides can also be applied through equipment which creates a mist by two opposing spinning discs driven by batteries in the handle of the machine.

MEDICAL SIGNIFICANCE

Human antibody reaction to the trauma and saliva of fleas when biting can be severe. Considerable irritation and swelling may ensue, with the risk of the bites being scratched and becoming infected. In some parts of the world, fleas will transmit sylvatic and epidemic plague, endemic typhus and other diseases to humans. If a flea carrying the infective stage of a cat or dog tapeworm (*Dipylidium caninum*) is swallowed by humans, the worm will develop in the gut. The female gravid jigger flea *Tunga penetrans* (found in tropical Africa and America) will burrow into human tissue, particularly the feet, to lay her eggs.

Plate 25 Flea larvae. Note the dark alimentary canal containing blood passed out by adult fleas in the bleeding site.

Plate 26 Adult bedbug *Cimex lectularius*.

Plate 27 Mortar in a room infested with *Cimex lectularius*. Adult and nymphal bedbugs, cast skins and hatched eggs can be seen.

Plate 28 Evidence of bedbug infestation on a bed-head.

Plate 29 Evidence of bedbug infestation on wall panelling above the bed.

Plate 30 An unusual photograph of a destitute's foot, showing excessively growing toe nails infested with bedbugs. A large number of bedbugs were removed from the room where this person lived. By courtesy of the Department of Medical Illustration, Manchester Royal Infirmary.

Plate 31 Male *Pediculus humanus corporis*, the human body louse.

Plate 32 Mother grooming her child for head lice. This is a common and accepted cosmetic practice in many parts of the world.

10
Bedbugs

Bedbugs belong to the Order Hempitera, a group of insects known as the 'bugs'. The vast majority of bugs are plant feeders, having mouthparts adapted for piercing vegetation and sucking fluids from the stems and leaves. Many bugs, such as aphids, are important agricultural pests and will carry a number of viral diseases from infected to uninfected crops.

Two families of bugs contain members whose mouthparts have become adapted to feeding on blood. The cone-nose bugs within the family Reduviidae (sub-family Triatominae and hence also known as reduviid or triatome bugs) occur only in the New World where they may transmit South American trypanosomiasis (sleeping sickness) or Chagas' disease. (This bug will be discussed on page 130.)

The other family of bloodsucking bugs is the Cimicidae containing the bedbugs (*Cimex* species) which feeds on humans, and similar bugs associated with the nests of swallows and other birds, as well as bats.

Bedbugs are temporary ectoparasites of humans and when not feeding on blood, will hide in cracks, crevices and other harbourages in human habitation. There are two species, *Cimex lectularius* (Plate 26), found in temperate regions throughout the world, and *Cimex hemipterus*, found mainly in the tropics and subtropics. There is, however, a considerable overlap of distribution. The two species are very similar in appearance and identical in life cycle and habits.

The bedbug is an oval flattened insect 4–5 mm in length (Fig. 10.1). When unfed it is a pale brown in colour but is a much darker brown when full of blood. The head is short and broad, has a pair of prominent antennae and a pair of small dark compound eyes. The long slender mouthparts (proboscis) are slung beneath the

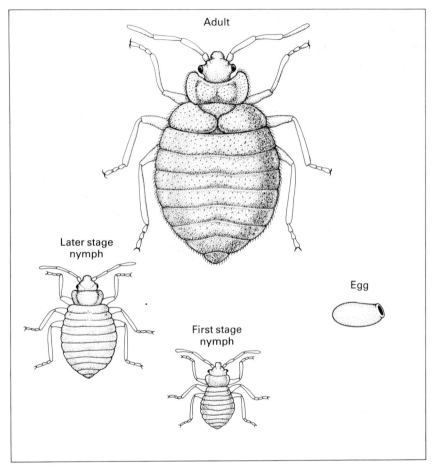

Fig. 10.1 *Cimex lectularius,* the bedbug. The life cycle is depicted, showing metamorphosis from the egg through to the adult form.

head and thorax between the front pair of legs when not in use. The front segment of the thorax is well developed and forms a pair of 'shoulders' (cusps) on either side of the head. (These provide the main diagnostic difference between the two species of bedbug, being more pronounced and flattened in *C lectularius* than in *C hemipterus*.)

The bedbug is secondarily wingless, having lost its wings during its evolution into a blood-sucking ectoparasite. All that remains is a pair of wing pads (hemielytra) on the top of the thorax. Three pairs of well developed legs enable the insect to crawl rapidly. The abdomen is large and conspicuously segmented. The tip of the abdomen is rounded in the female and more pointed in the male with a curved penis at the end.

LIFE CYCLE

The bedbug is closely associated with humans and the human environment throughout its life cycle, which is one of incomplete metamophosis. After mating, the female will lay two or three eggs every day for the rest of her life which may last several weeks or even months, thus she will lay several hundred eggs during her lifetime. The eggs are laid in cracks and crevices in furniture (including beds), walls and panelling, behind loose wallpaper and on brickwork (Plate 27). The egg is about 1 mm long, yellowish white and vase-shaped, with a lid (operculum) at one end (see Fig. 10.1). Eggs will hatch in about ten days at room temperature (20°C), more quickly at higher temperatures (seven days at 25°C) and not for several weeks at lower temperatures. They will not hatch at all below 14°C.

There are five nymphal stages and each will take one or more bloodmeals. The immature phase will last about six weeks, but may be considerably longer under adverse conditions, at cooler temperatures or in the absence of bloodmeals. Adults, both male and female, will also feed exclusively on blood. Human blood is preferred at all stages, but if it is not available blood from rodents, rabbits, bats and birds may be taken.

HABITS

Bloodfeeding will be carried out at night while the host is sleeping. The bedbug will crawl from its nearby hiding place and spend several minutes taking a bloodmeal, considerably increasing the girth of its abdomen. It may even reach its host by dropping on it from above. After feeding, the bedbug will crawl back into its harbourage and begin to remove excess fluid by evacuating semi-digested blood as faeces. This appears as dark spots or smears around the hiding place and is a good indication of an infestation (Plates 28 and 29). At the same site, though probably better hidden, will be eggs, empty egg cases and cast nymphal skins. It may also be possible to detect a sickly sweet smell typical of bedbug infestation.

MEDICAL SIGNIFICANCE

Although all stages of bedbug rely entirely on blood for their nutrition, they do not act as natural vectors of any human disease. However, the bite of the bug causes considerable irritation and swelling in susceptible humans and may result in significant loss of sleep and lowering of general health and morale. Heavy infestations are usually associated with dilapidated dwellings and poor standards of hygiene, to the extent that the bedbugs may actually be found harbouring on the human body in extreme cases (Plate 30).

Being wingless, their power of dispersal is limited, but infestations may arise from buying infested secondhand furniture or carrying bedbugs from an infested site on suitcases and other belongings. The area of the body which shows bites is often significant in diagnosing the cause, and it may be the first indication of an infestation when the victim reports to the doctor's surgery. Bites on parts of the body which are uncovered at night (face, neck, shoulders and arms) are indicative of bedbug presence.

CONTROL MEASURES

Bedbugs are more difficult to control than cockroaches, because they tend to hide deeper in their harbourages. Unfed bugs are extremely flat and can crawl far into cracks and crevices, remaining there for several months without food under adverse conditions. Their presence is usually easy to detect by the faecal spots, eggs and cast skins. They may be attracted to a potential bloodmeal by the exhaled carbon-dioxide of a likely host, and they can be encouraged to leave hiding by blowing into the harbourage. A pyrethrins aerosol will have the same excitatory effect.

Surfaces over which bedbugs will crawl to reach the host should be sprayed with a residual insecticide. Furniture, particularly bedframes, cupboards and inside chests of drawers, can be similarly treated. Mattresses may be sprayed but should be dried and aired before reuse. Bedding and clothing can be put in a tumble drier at the normal drying temperature, which will kill any bedbugs and eggs present.

11

Lice

The control of human lice will probably be carried out under medical advice. However, proprietary insecticides are readily available to the public, and information may sometimes be sought from those involved in pest control.

Lice are permanent ectoparasites of warm blooded animals and are characteristically specific in their choice of host. They cannot survive for more than a day or two away from their chosen host, and each species of louse is confined to a particular species of mammal or bird.

Lice are classified according to their feeding habits: those which chew skin, fur and feathers in the Order Mallophaga, and those which suck blood in the Anoplura. The chewing lice rarely infest humans, whereas three types of sucking lice will feed exclusively on human blood.

PEDICULUS HUMANUS

This species occurs as two varieties, *P humanus capitis* (the head louse) and *P humanus corporis* (the body louse), sometimes treated as two separate species (Fig. 11.1). They are very similar in appearance but biologically they are very different; the head louse is found only on the hair of the head, sucking blood from the scalp, whereas the body louse lives on the underclothing and feeds on the body (Plate 31).

The adult louse is 2–4 mm in length, greyish in colour but red-brown when fed. It is elongate, wingless and dorsoventrally flattened, with a distinct head, narrower than the thorax, short antennae and a pair of simple eyes. The sucking mouthparts are telescoped inside the head when not in use. The thorax is distinct, with six legs, each terminating in a strong claw. The abdomen is

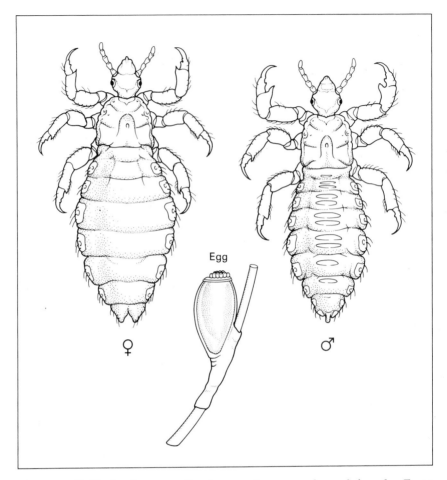

Egg

♀   ♂

Fig. 11.1 *Pediculus humanus,* the human louse, male and female. From the egg to the adult form.

segmented, with darker plates, and has a bilobed ending in the female; in the male the pointed aedeagus (penis) protrudes from the end of the abdomen. Headlice are usually smaller than body lice, but otherwise there are only minor anatomical differences.

Life cycle and habits

All lice undergo an incomplete metamorphosis in their life cycle and will spend their entire life on their preferred host. Thus, the gravid human head louse, having mated on the host, will lay about six pinkish eggs a day, glued individually to the base of the hair. The body louse will glue her eggs to seams and threads of clothing. Female lice live for about one month, laying 200–300 eggs during that time. The egg hatches within a week and the pale-coloured empty case, known as a nit, remains firmly fixed to hair or clothing. Human hair grows at a rate of about 1 cm a month, thus the position of the nit on the hair shaft will give a good indication of the duration of infestation. The young nymph requires a bloodmeal within a few hours of hatching, and will feed several times a day as it develops through three immature stages to the adult in about ten days. All stages and both sexes feed exclusively on blood.

Medical significance

Because of their bloodsucking habits, an infestation of human lice, known as pediculosis, may cause considerable irritation. Scratching of the bites may give rise to secondary infection. The body louse may transmit typhus, trench fever and relapsing fever. The head louse does not transmit disease in nature (Plate 32).

Control

Lice are transmitted from one person to another by close bodily contact and perhaps very occasionally via infested clothing and other articles. They are not necessarily more common on dirty heads or bodies; it is simply that in this situation they are less likely to be noticed and hence controlled. There is no correlation between infestation and hair length.

Head lice can easily be controlled by the application of an insecticidal lotion formulated for this purpose. The active ingredient is usually malathion or carbaryl (which will kill all stages including the eggs), and it is important to follow the label instructions. Shampoos are also available, but lotions are much more effective. All members of a household should be treated at the same time. Body lice can be controlled by the use of an approved insecticidal dust such as 1% malathion. Clothing should be washed in hot water (over 60°C) and then ironed.

PHTHIRUS PUBIS

The pubic louse *Phthirus pubis* (Fig. 11.2 and Plate 33) is also known as the crab louse because of its shape. This louse infests the coarser,

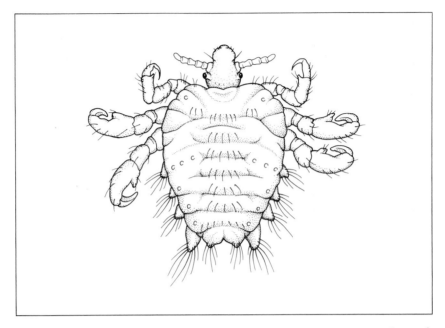

Fig. 11.2 *Phthirus pubis*, the pubic louse. This is also known as the crab louse because of its shape.

less dense hairs of the human body, in particular the pubic region. It may be found on any hairy part of the body including the beard and eye lashes but rarely on the scalp.

The pubic louse is approximately 2 mm in length, greyish in colour but darker when fed, and short and broad in shape – somewhat resembling a miniature crab. It has a distinct head with short antennae and simple eyes, but the thorax and abdomen are fused. The legs, particularly the middle and hind pairs, end in large claws used for gripping the hairs. It is the shape and position of these claws which probably confine the crab louse to the coarser, more widely spaced body hairs.

Life cycle and habits

The gravid female crab louse will lay her eggs often gluing several to each hair (Plate 34). The life cycle is very similar to that of the human louse and all stages feed exclusively on blood.

Medical significance

The pubic louse does not transmit disease. However, an infestation known as phthiriasis or 'crabs' may cause considerable discomfort and sometimes embarrassment, since it is typically acquired by close contact, usually sexual intercourse, with an infested person.

Control

Pubic lice can be controlled with the same lotions used for head lice, such as malathion or carbaryl. It is only necessary to shave the hair if there is a known allergic response to these insecticides causing a dermatitis.

12

Bees, wasps and ants

●

This group of insects belongs to the Order Hymenoptera. All undergo a complete metamorphosis and a number of species are social, living in colonies, nests or hives. Some have the ovipositor adapted to stinging. Others occur in large numbers, causing problems in domestic and catering situations because of their foraging habits, when the workers collect food to feed the reproducing queen in the nest. For these reasons it may sometimes be necessary to take control measures. However, the vast majority of Hymenoptera, particularly the honey bees, are highly beneficial in their role as pollinators, and measures should only be undertaken (a) to remove a wasp nest from a domestic or similar situation, (b) to control nuisance garden ants, and (c) to control infestations of Pharaoh's ants.

WASPS

The common wasps, *Vespula vulgaris* and *V germanica* (Fig. 12.1) are about 14 mm in length and brightly banded in black and yellow. The much maligned hornet, *Vespa crabro*, perhaps the least aggressive of wasps, is considerably larger and marked in yellow and brown.

The queen wasp, somewhat larger than the worker, emerges from hibernation in the spring and builds a round nest 2–3 inches in diameter from chewed wood pulp. In this she lays eggs from which hatch pale grubs; these are fed on insects captured by the queen. After a few weeks they pupate; the adult workers emerge and take over building the nest and feeding the queen. The queen concentrates on producing large numbers of eggs. Towards the end of the season, new queens are produced which form colonies the following year, while other members of the colony die.

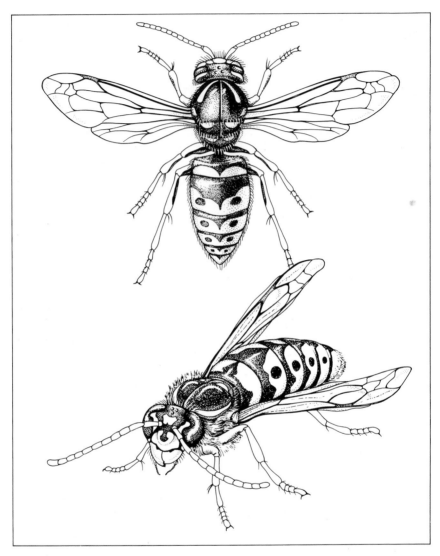

Fig. 12.1 Worker *Vespula vulgaris*, the common wasp. Top and side views.

A nest may contain several thousand wasps. It is often built below ground in a garden, in a roof space or attic where the wasps may have considerable and unwanted contact with humans. In the late summer, scavenging wasps turn their attention to ripe fruit, jams and other sweet substances. Apart from the nuisance they cause, their stings can often be painful, although they usually only sting if provoked.

Control

Destruction of the nest is the only satisfactory method of control. In an enclosed space, such as a loft, the use of an insecticidal smoke generator is effective. In other areas an insecticidal dust may be applied to the nest itself and the surrounding surfaces. If possible, control measures should be carried out at night when all wasps are in the nest, and suitable protective precautions should be taken as the wasps may become aggressive when disturbed.

GARDEN ANTS (*LASIUS NIGER*)

Worker ants are 3–5 mm in length, and dark brown to black in colour (Fig. 12.2). They will forage from the nest which is usually outside in a flower bed or under paving stones. They may cause a nuisance by entering kitchens while scavenging for sweet food to take back to the queen in the nest.

Control

This can often be achieved by following the trail to the nest and pouring boiling water over it. Alternatively, a poison bait containing boric acid powder or some other insecticide can be made available to the scavenging ants so that they take it back to the nest and feed it to the queen, thus destroying the reproductive colony. The workers can be killed with a spray of residual insecticide, but this does not reach the source of the problem. In mid to late summer the colony will swarm, causing a particular nuisance: winged males and females will leave the nest, mate and take flight. The males soon die, while the females lose their wings and hibernate to form new colonies the following year. Swarming is a transient nuisance, lasting only two to three days, but it may be the way in which new colonies are formed. Alternatively, particularly with Pharaoh's ant (see below), workers and queens may migrate from a large colony, taking eggs and pupae with them; also, infested material may be introduced into a new habitat.

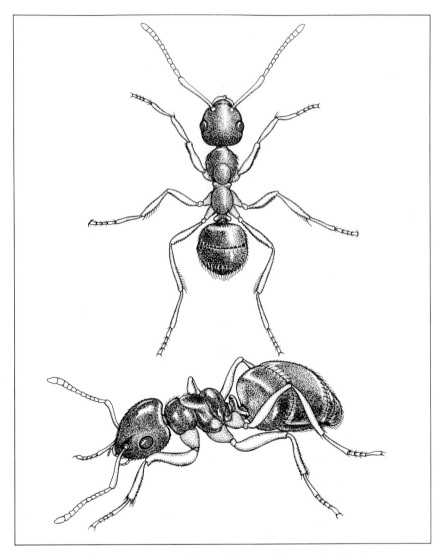

Fig. 12.2 Worker *Lasius niger*, the garden ant. Top and side views.

PHARAOH'S ANT (*MONOMORIUM PHARAONIS*)

Worker ants are 2 mm in length, yellow-brown in colour, sometimes with a darker abdomen (Fig. 12.3). Pharaoh's ant is tropical in origin, therefore in temperate climates it requires artificial heat in order to survive and reproduce. Colonies containing several queens are formed deep in the structure of a suitable building; the workers will forage for sweet and proteinaceous food scraps to take to the queens. Scavenging ants may be a considerable nuisance; they may also damage packaging by their feeding habits, sometimes chewing through the plastic bags protecting sterilized dressings and instruments in hospitals.

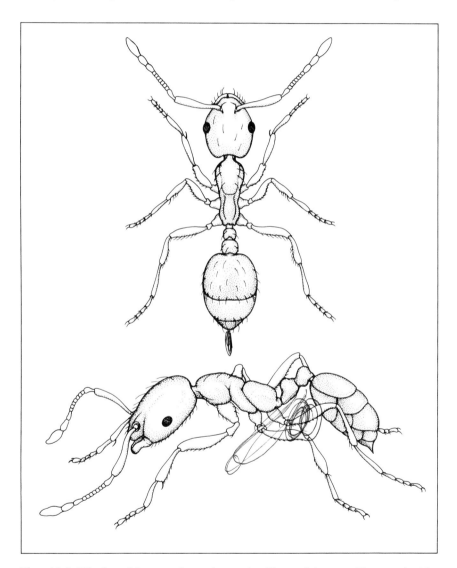

Fig. 12.3 Worker *Monomorium pharaonis*, Pharaoh's ant. Top and side views.

Control

It is essential to kill the queen ants in the nest to achieve control of Pharaoh' ants. Residual sprays will only kill the foraging workers, and the queens will go on reproducing. A poison bait containing boric acid may be used, but this will often kill the worker ant before it can regurgitate the material in the nest. The insect growth regulator analogue methoprene is the most effective material available. This is mixed with substances attractive to the worker ants, such as sponge cake, honey or liver powder, and placed in 2-inch lengths of plastic tubing (half inch in diameter) to reduce dessication, in areas where the ants are foraging. Ant runs should first be located by placing unbaited material in likely positions overnight and looking for empty tubes or foraging ants the following morning. The manufacturer's instructions should be followed carefully, and one bait tube will cover an area of $3\,m^2$. Tubes can be fixed to vertical surfaces with sticky tape.

The worker ants will take the bait back to the nest to feed to the queens, and the growth regulator will cause her ovaries to atrophy, halting her egg production. While being very effective, this method will take 15–20 weeks to eradicate the infestation, thus patience on the part of the operator, and particularly the customer, is essential. It is also important to explain the principle of the method to the client. Bait tubes should be replaced if they become dried out and thus unpalatable to the worker ants. After about six weeks, a residual spray may be applied for cosmetic reasons to kill the foraging workers, but it is preferable that this is delayed as much as possible.

13

Beetles

The beetles form the largest of the insect Orders, the Coleoptera. They are extremely varied in size, shape and habits. Most adult beetles have two pairs of wings, the front pair being horny and covering the membranous hind pair when folded over the abdomen, forming a median longitudinal line where they meet. They typically have well developed chewing mouthparts.

Only a few species are of public health significance, feeding on stored food products, clothing, furnishings and wood. Beetles go through a complete metamorphosis in their life cycle, and it is often only the larval stage which causes damage. Beetle larvae have a conspicuous head capsule and six legs on the thorax. They do not have the stumpy false legs (pseudopods) which moth and butterfly caterpillars have on the abdomen (Plate 35).

Described below are the most common species found as pests in domestic premises and infesting stored food and other commodities.

STEGOBIUM PANICEUM

Stegobium paniceum, the biscuit beetle, is 2–3 mm in length and reddish-brown in colour, covered in short hairs, with antennae about one-third the length of the oval-shaped body (Fig. 13.1). The adult may live indoors but does not feed there. The larva is maggot-like, with a dark head capsule and legs. It will attack cereals, biscuits, flour and spices, damaging containers in shops, stores and domestic premises.

ANTHRENUS VERBASCI

Anthrenus verbasci, the carpet beetle, is 3 mm in length, oval in shape, with short clubbed antennae (Fig. 13.2). The body is dark

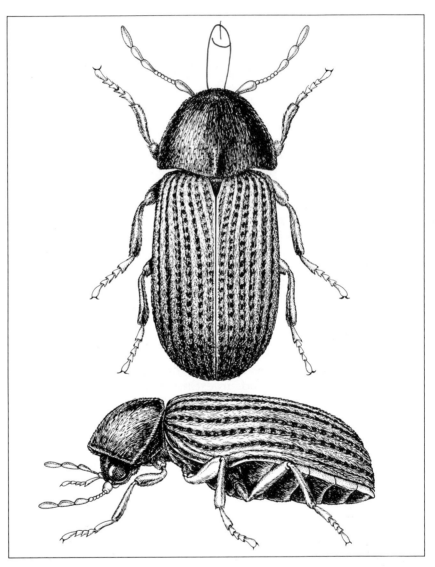

Fig. 13.1 *Stegobium paniceum*, the biscuit beetle. Top and side views.

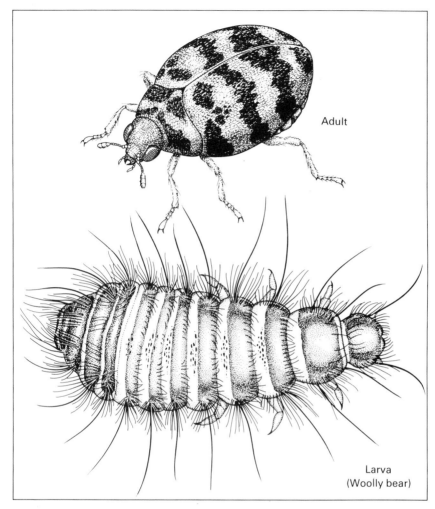

Adult

Larva
(Woolly bear)

Fig. 13.2 *Anthrenus verbasci*, the carpet beetle. Adult and larva.

brown or black, mottled with patches of yellow or white scales. The adult will live out-of-doors feeding on plants, but the female will lay eggs indoors on the larval food material which is always of animal origin.

The larval stage is known as 'woolly bear', stubby and dark in colour with segmental tufts of long, arrow-headed bristles. It will feed on and damage woollen fabrics, carpets and clothes, even those of a wool/nylon mixture, but will not attack pure synthetic fibres. The carpet beetle is a serious pest of museum collections. It may be found in birds' nests which may be the source of infestation.

ATTAGENUS PELLIO

Attagenus pellio, the fur beetle, is 5 mm in length, with short, clubbed antennae. It is black in colour, with a patch of whitish hairs

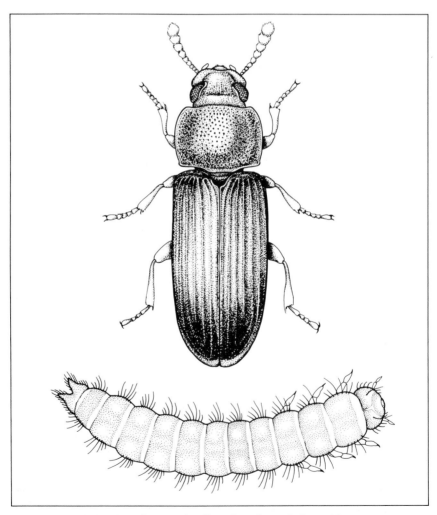

Fig. 13.3 *Tribolium confusum*, the flour beetle. Adult and larva.

in the middle of each wing-case, and a simple eye between the two compound eyes. The larva is similar to that of the carpet beetle but more elongate and with longer bristles on the back end. It will feed on all fabrics containing wool, and will also damage furs and hides.

TRIBOLIUM CONFUSUM

Tribolium confusum, the flour beetle, (Fig. 13.3) is 3–4 mm in length, reddish-brown in colour, with short clubbed antennae. The body is

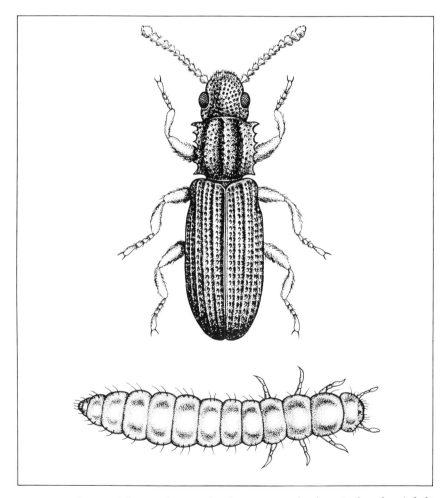

Fig. 13.4 *Oryzaephilus surinamensis*, the saw-toothed grain beetle. Adult and larva.

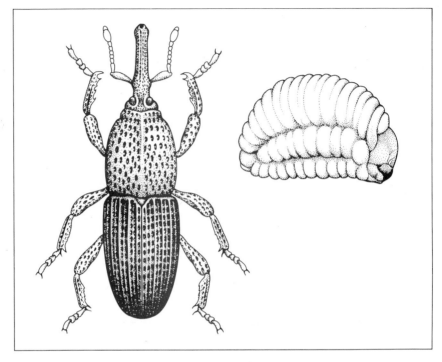

Fig. 13.5 *Sitophilus granarius*, the grain weevil. Adult and larva.

covered in small pits, giving it a dotted appearance, but it has no apparent hairs or scales. The larva is long and thin, yellowish-brown in colour. Both larva and adult attack a wide range of cereal products, nuts and dried fruit, and are found in granaries, mills, bakeries and kitchens. A very similar species with shorter clubbed antennae is *T castaneum*, the rust-red flour beetle.

ORYZAEPHILUS SURINAMENSIS

Oryzaephilus surinamensis, the saw-toothed grain beetle (Fig. 13.4), is 3 mm in length, elongate in shape, with serrated (saw-toothed) edges to its thorax. It is dark brown in colour, with medium length clubbed antennae. The larva is slender, similar but smaller than the larva of *Tribolium*. Both adult and larva will cause damage to cereal and rice products as well as dried fruit.

SITOPHILUS GRANARIUS

Sitophilus granarius, the grain weevil, (Fig. 13.5) is 2–4 mm in length, including the prominent snout protruding from the front of the head. The appearance is a shiny pitted dark brown to black. The grub-like larva feeds entirely inside a grain of cereal where it pupates, the adult beetle emerging through a hole in the surface. Adults will also feed on grain and cereal products.

DERMESTID BEETLES

This group in the genus *Dermestes* includes *D lardarius* (Fig. 13.6),

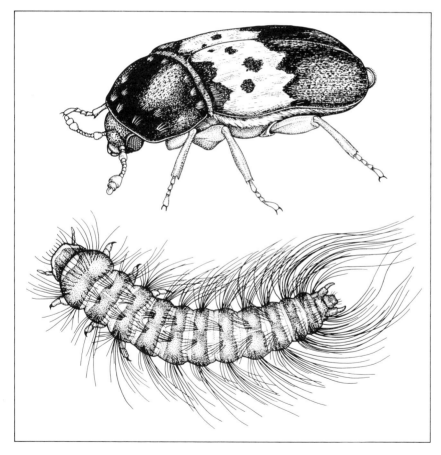

Fig. 13.6 *Dermestes lardarius*, of the Dermestid family. Adult and larva. Commonly known as larder or bacon beetle.

the larder or bacon beetle, and *D maculatus*, the hide or bone beetle. The adult is oval and up to 12 mm in length, with short clubbed antennae. The body is dark in colour with lighter markings which form a continuous light band across the body of *D lardarius*.

The larva is dark brown and covered segmentally with tufts of hair of varying length, but without the long tail hairs of *Attagenus* or *Anthrenus*, which are also shorter and smaller in size.

Adult *Dermestes* cause little damage, but larvae will eat into any material of animal origin including fur, hides, wool, bones and meat. They may be found in birds' nests and other debris.

TENEBRIO MOLITOR

Tenebrio molitor, the meal-worm beetle, (Fig. 13.7) is 15 mm in length, black in colour, with medium length unclubbed antennae

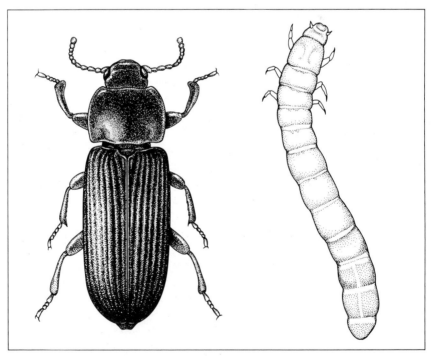

Fig. 13.7 *Tenebrio molitor*, the meal-worm beetle. Adult and larva.

and a shouldered thorax. The larva is up to 30 mm long, usually yellowish in colour, though sometimes darker brown, and without bristles. Adults and larvae will feed on cereals and cereal products, but in general they cause less damage than smaller species of beetle pests.

PTINUS TECTUS

Ptinus tectus, the spider beetle, (Fig. 13.8) is 2–4 mm in length, with a rounded appearance, long clubbed antennae and head slung beneath the thorax, giving it somewhat the shape of a tiny spider. The body is densely covered with tiny hairs. The larva is pale and grub-like in appearance, and may attack a wide variety of stored foods, spinning a cocoon in which it pupates.

Control of stored-product beetle pests

Whatever the species of beetle causing the problem, the same principles of control apply. All infested commodities must be removed and destroyed by burning, without spreading the infestation further. Adjacent commodities should be carefully inspected and similarly destroyed if there is any suspicion of infestation. The room or building should be thoroughly cleaned and vacuumed, taking care to ensure that all levels are dealt with. Fabrics and structure can then be treated with an insecticidal preparation approved for this particular use; instructions will be given on the label. Emulsion concentrates or wettable powders containing, for example, fenitrothion or pirimiphos-methyl may be used.

If the scale of infestation makes destruction of the commodity economically unviable, the container (storeroom, warehouse) and contents may be fumigated with methyl bromide gas. A special licence and proper training are required before fumigation can be carried out. It is essential to inspect all in-coming goods for signs of infestation, to prevent a recurrence of the problem. Existing stocks should be checked regularly and kept well ventilated, since it is often the moulds or fungus growing in damp situations which encourage pests in the first instance.

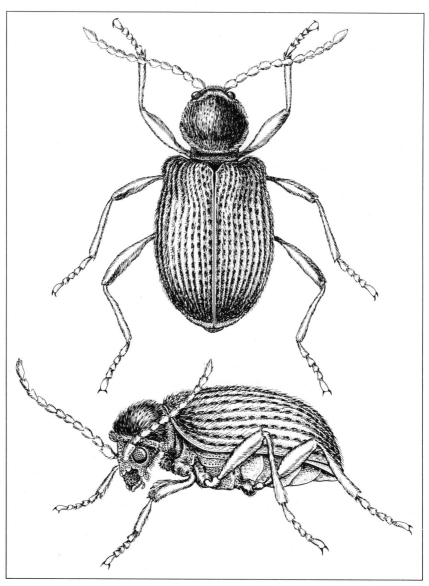

Fig. 13.8 *Ptinus tectus*, the Australian spider beetle. Top and side views.

WOOD-BORING BEETLES

Several species of beetle, mainly in their larval stages, will attack timber. The most common of these is the furniture beetle *Anobium punctatum* (Fig. 13.9), the larva of which is commonly known as the woodworm. The adult beetle is 3–5 mm in length, dark in colour with a somewhat hump-backed appearance and medium length unclubbed antennae.

The gravid female will lay eggs in cracks in timber and will also use the exit holes left by an emerging previous generation. The larva will burrow into the wood, feeding particularly on sap wood with a high moisture but low resin content. It may take over three years to develop through its larval stages and will pupate in the timber, emerging through the characteristic exit hole about 1.5–2 mm in diameter. Furniture, beams and other structural timber

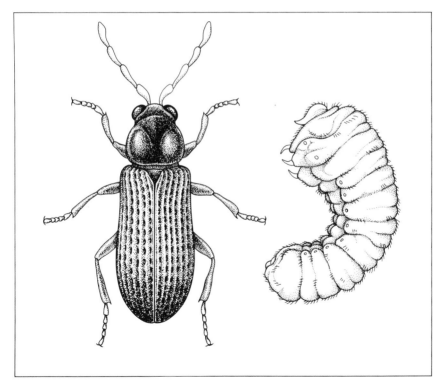

Fig. 13.9 *Anobium punctatum*, the furniture beetle. This is the most common of the wood-boring beetles. Adult and larva.

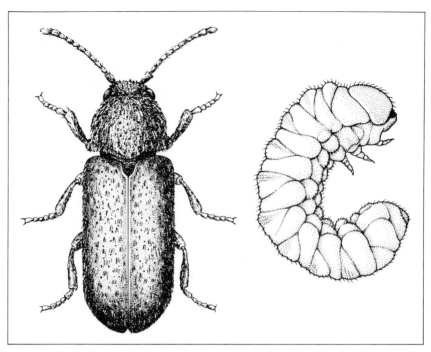

Fig. 13.10 *Xestobium rufovillosum,* the death watch beetle. Adult and larva.

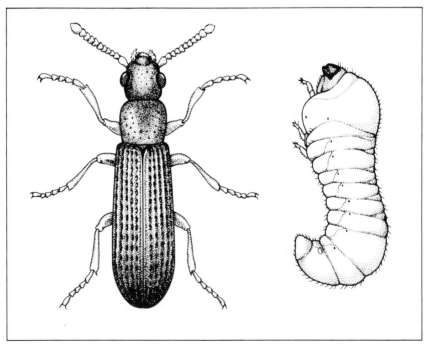

Fig. 13.11 Powder-post beetle, which belongs to the genus *Lyctus*. Adult and larva.

may be damaged in this way. Dust from the bore-hole, known as frass, characteristically consists of lemon-shaped gritty pellets.

Other species of beetle which may damage timber are the death watch beetle *Xestobium rufovillosum* (Fig. 13.10), the wood-boring weevils *Pentarthrum huttoni* and *Euphyrum confine*, the powder-post beetles in the genus *Lyctus* (Fig. 13.11) and the house longhorn beetle *Hylotrupes bajulus* (Fig. 13.12).

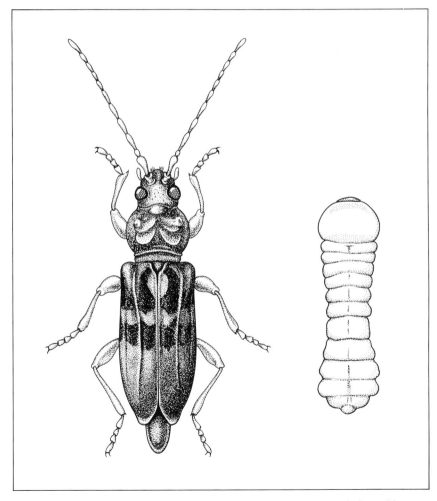

Fig. 13.12 *Hylotrupes bajulus*, the house longhorn beetle. Adult and larva.

Control of wood-boring beetles

Control of wood-boring beetles involves treating the infested timber or furniture with a liquid insecticide which may be brushed or sprayed on to the surface or injected into the wood through existing exit holes. Impregnation or dipping of timber, particularly by vacuum treatment, will discourage the larval stages from feeding. Surface treatment with a residual spray will only dissuade gravid females from egg-laying or perhaps kill adults as they emerge. Timber may also be fumigated.

Where the infestation has rendered structural timber unsound, it must be removed and burnt and replaced with pretreated sound timber. The control of woodworm should only be undertaken by someone with specialist knowledge of this aspect of the pest control profession, and is not within the scope of this book.

14
Moths

Moths and butterflies make up the Order Lepidoptera which includes some of the largest and most beautiful of all insects. All Lepidoptera go through a complete metamorphosis, eggs being laid on the food plant or other material on which the caterpillar-like larval stages feed. In addition to the true legs on the thorax, these larvae have several pairs of stumpy false legs (pseudopods) on the abdomen (in comparison with the beetle larvae which do not have pseudopods). The pupal stage is in the form of a chrysalis, often in a web or cocoon.

Household Moths

The larvae of three common species of moth typically feed on materials containing wool, and may cause considerable damage to fabrics. These are the clothes moth *Tineola bisselliella* (Fig. 14.1), the brown house moth *Hofmannophila pseudospretella* (Fig. 14.2), and the white-shouldered house moth *Endrosis sarcitrella* (Fig. 14.3). All are 8–10 mm in length, the clothes moth being the smallest and whitish in colour, whereas the house moths are a mottled buff to dark brown, the white shouldered house moth having a pale anterior portion.

The larvae are whitish caterpillars with a dark head capsule and longish body hairs. The larval period will depend on the environmental situation, and may be only two to three months, but up to four years in adverse conditions. Larvae will feed on the wool content of clothes, blankets, carpets, uniforms etc. causing holes and considerable damage. House moth larvae will also feed on cereals. Eggs will be laid on the larval food material.

Control of clothes moths can be achieved by removing and destroying infested articles and by treating carpets etc. with a

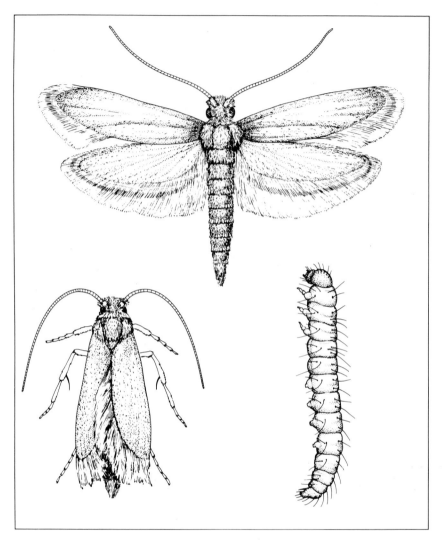

Fig. 14.1 *Tineola bisselliella*, the clothes moth. Adult and larva.

residual insecticide approved for this purpose. Infestation can be prevented by layering clothes with naphthalene crystals or mothballs and ensuring that cloths and carpets are not soiled with sugary substances which attract egg laying.

Moths as stored-product pests
The larvae of several species of moths will feed on a wide variety of

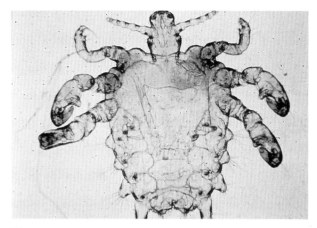

Plate 33 *Phthirus pubis*, the pubic or crab louse.

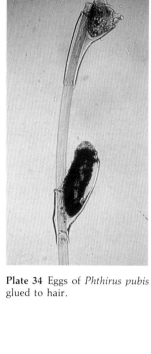

Plate 34 Eggs of *Phthirus pubis* glued to hair.

Plate 35 Weevil *Bruchus* species on dried peas. Note the holes in grain, caused by emerging adult beetles. Their larvae have fed on the grain and pupated.

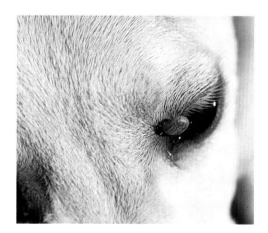

Plate 36 Engorging female hard tick feeding on a dog.

Plate 37 Mouthparts of hard tick.

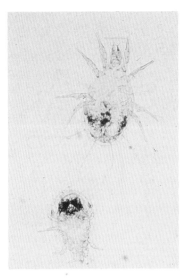

Plate 38 Allergy-causing mite *Cheyletiella* species.

Plate 39 *Demodex folliculorum*, the hair follicle mite. By courtesy of Dr S Selwyn.

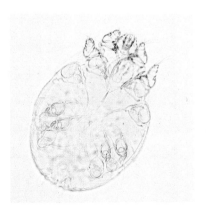

Plate 40 *Sarcoptes scabiei*, the scabies mite.

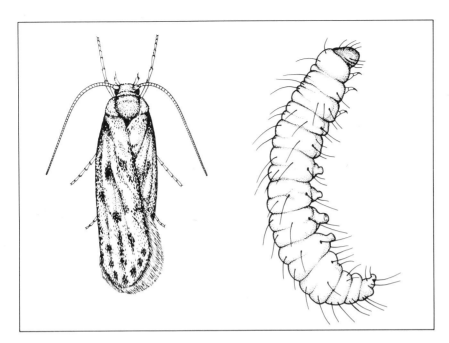

Fig. 14.2 *Hofmannophila pseudospretella*, the brown house moth. Adult and larva.

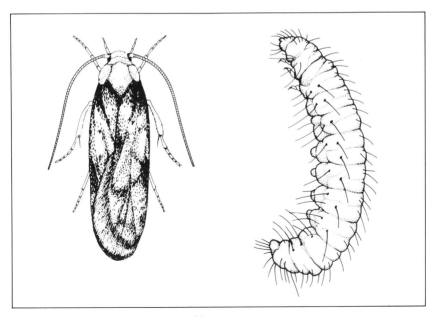

Fig. 14.3 *Endrosis sarcitrella*, the white-shouldered house moth. Adult and larva.

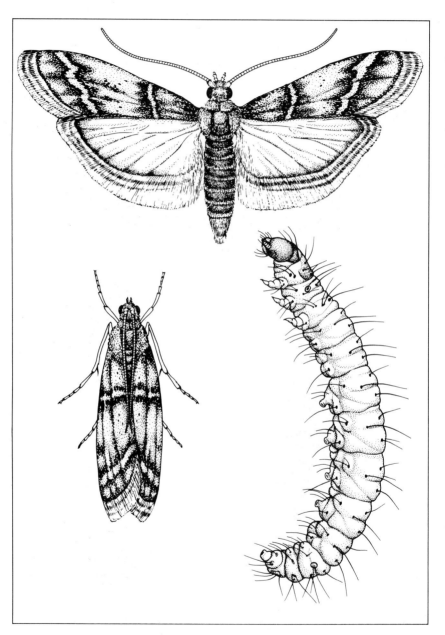

Fig. 14.4 *Ephestia elutella*, the warehouse moth. Larva and adult.

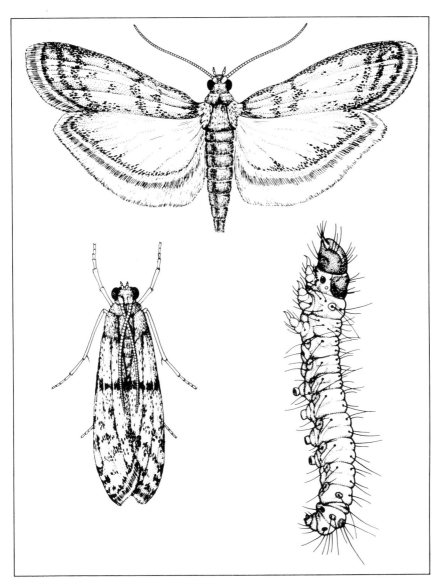

Fig. 14.5 *Ephestia cautella*, the tropical warehouse moth. Larva and adult.

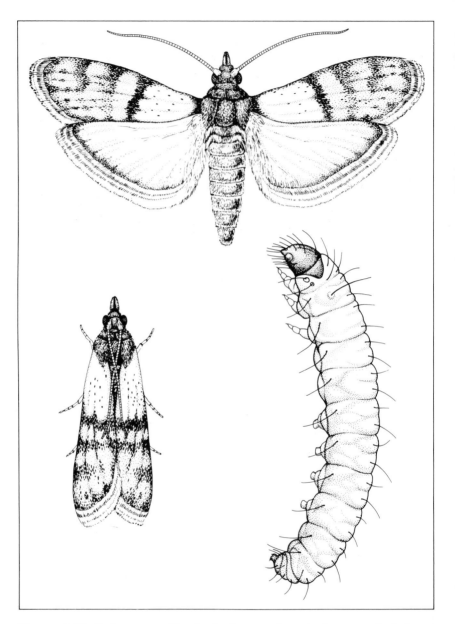

Fig. 14.6 *Plodia interpunctella*, the Indian meal moth. Larva and adult.

foods including cereals and cereal products, dried fruit, spices, chocolate and nuts. These are the warehouse moth *Ephestia elutella* (Fig. 14.4) and the tropical warehouse moth *Ephestia cautella* (Fig. 14.5), the Indian meal moth *Plodia interpunctella* (Fig. 14.6) and the mill moth *Ephestia kuehniella* (Fig. 14.7). All are about 12 mm wingspan, with the mill moth being the smallest, and all are a

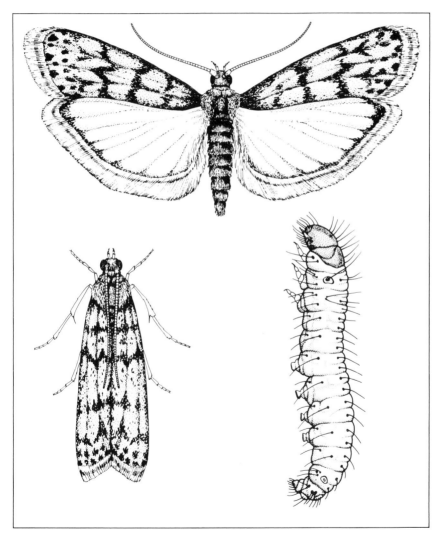

Fig. 14.7 *Ephestia kuehniella*, the mill moth. Larva and adult.

a mottled grey except the Indian meal moth which has wings reddish brown at the tip and pale buff at the base.

The larvae are all a creamy white, and when fully fed they typically migrate to cracks and crevices surrounding the food supply. There they spin cocoons in which they pupate. Control of stored product moths can be achieved in the same way as beetle pests, by removing infested materials, thoroughly cleaning and treating with a residual insecticide.

15

Miscellaneous invertebrate pests

From time to time, those involved in pest control may be asked to control or advise on a variety of invertebrate animals which cause an occasional nuisance. These are discussed briefly in this chapter.

LEPISMA SACCHARINA AND *THERMOBIA DOMESTICA*

The Silverfish *Lepisma saccharina* (Fig. 15.1) and Firebrat *Thermobia domestica* (Fig. 15.2) are both members of the Order Thysanura or bristletails. They are primitive, carrot-shaped, wingless insects, with long antennae and three tail-like appendages at the tip of the abdomen. Development is gradual through as many as 60 moults,

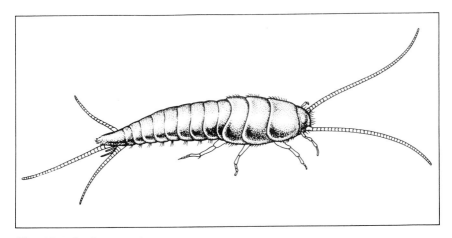

Fig. 15.1 *Lepisma saccharina,* the Silverfish.

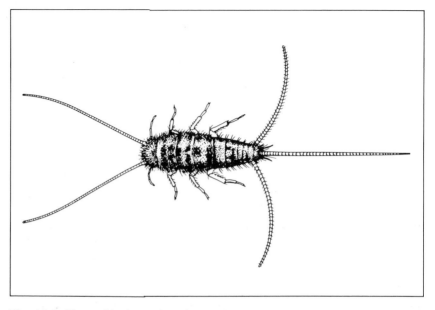

Fig. 15.2 *Thermobia domestica,* the Firebrat.

but reproduction may begin after only 12–15 moults. The three 'tails' appear after only a few moults.

The silver-fish is silvery-white in colour, and about 12 mm in length when fully grown. It will normally live under leaves, bark or stones but may also be found in cool, damp domestic situations where it feeds on moulds growing around wash basins and tiling.

The firebrat is greyish in colour with darker speckled markings and somewhat larger than the silverfish, up to about 15 mm in length. It is found in warm conditions, and flourishes in kitchens and bakeries at temperatures of over 37°C.

Control

Silverfish can be controlled by raising the temperature and lowering the humidity of the environment, coupled with improving conditions of hygiene. Conversely, the firebrat will not survive if the temperature is lowered to below 15°C. The use of residual insecticides is effective, although several treatments may be necessary. Sticky traps (see page 20) may also be useful.

ACHETA DOMESTICUS (HOUSE CRICKET)

Crickets belong to the insectan Order Orthoptera which also includes the long-horned and short-horned grasshoppers (Fig. 15.3). Adult crickets fold their wings around the abdomen, whereas grasshoppers hold the wings obliquely over the abdomen like the roof of a house. All go through an incomplete metamorphosis, the nymphs being wingless. The adult house cricket is light brown in colour, 12–20 mm in length, with long antennae and well developed hind legs. A darting running movement is normal, jumping only being used as a method of escape, and flight is never achieved.

The life cycle from egg to adult, passing through as many as ten moults, may take up to nine months, although adults will live for only a few weeks. House crickets, being tropical in origin, will prefer a warm environment, sometimes living out-of-doors in the summer but coming into houses and catering units in the colder weather. Once established, they will remain indoors throughout the year, all stages feeding on any available soft food material. The adult males may cause a considerable nuisance and even distress by their loud chirruping, made by rasping the front wing against the hind wing on either side as a sexual attractant to the female cricket.

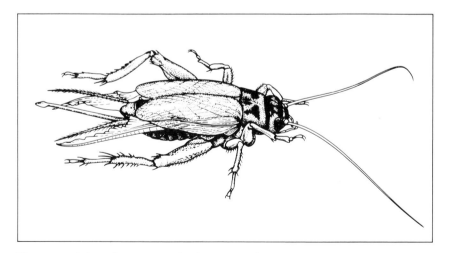

Fig. 15.3 *Acheta domesticus*, the house cricket.

Crickets can be controlled in a similar manner to cockroaches, by the use of residual insecticidal sprays or dusts on floors and harbourages in kitchens etc., and outside on rubbish tips and refuse areas which should be kept in a hygienic condition.

EARWIGS

These belong to the Order Dermaptera. Only two species commonly occur in Britain, namely *Forficula auricularia* (Fig. 15.4) which is 10–14 mm long with pincer-like cerci 4–9 mm long, and

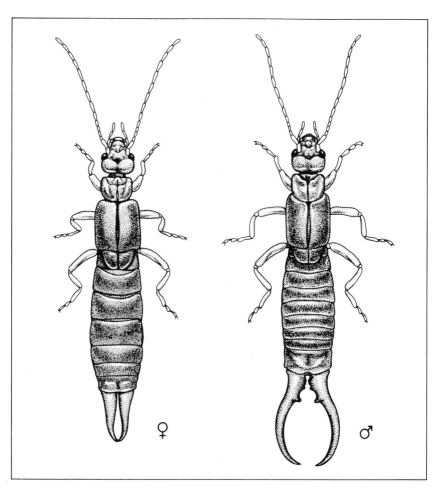

Fig. 15.4 *Forficula auricularia*, the Earwig.

Labia minor, 5 mm long with 2 mm pincers. They are nocturnal insects which feed on plants and small invertebrates, hiding during daylight in crevices often above ground level. The wings are folded neatly into wing-cases and are rarely, if ever, used.

Earwigs may occasionally enter houses at night searching for and fouling food. They can be controlled by applying insecticidal dust around likely entry points such as door steps, window sills and ventilation points.

BOOKLICE

Booklice (Psocids) (Fig. 15.5) form a small Order of insects, Psocoptera. They are minute, yellowish or greyish, soft-bodied creatures, the male being smaller than the female. Metamorphosis

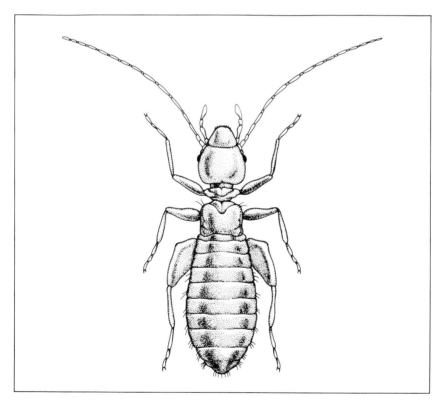

Fig. 15.5 Booklouse, of the Psocid Order.

is incomplete, and booklice may pass through up to eight nymphal stages. They require a diet rich in carbohydrates to proliferate, and may be found feeding on moulds on damp wallpaper, book bindings and furniture. They can be controlled by improving the environmental conditions and standards of hygiene. A knock-down aerosol will kill any live insects.

TERMITES

Termites (Fig. 15.6) in the Order Isoptera, undergo an incomplete metamorphosis in their life cycle. Although commonly known as 'White Ants', they are not related to the true ants in the Order Hymenoptera. Most species are tropical, but a few occur in temperate areas of Europe and North America where their burrowing and wood-eating habits may be very destructive. Three groups (families) are important in temperate regions, the damp wood termites (Termopsidae), the dry wood termites (Kalo-termitidae) and the subterranean termites (Rhinotermitidae). None have yet spread to Britain.

Termites live in colonies. The nymphs, which hatch from eggs laid by the queen, help to build the colony which may take several years to complete. They develop into workers or soldiers and eventually become winged. Mated females migrate to form new colonies.

Damp wood termites form small colonies which attack wood with a high moisture content. They are often found in fallen conifers and buildings in damp areas, where colonies are formed inside the timber and the frass discharged through holes to the exterior. Dry wood termites will infest drier timber and cause similar damage to structures and buildings. Subterranean termites form much larger colonies in the ground below timber and build communicating tubes to the structure above into which they burrow. A colony may house many thousands of individuals. This group of termites in particular may present a serious threat to timber-framed buildings, furniture, books etc. in many parts of the world.

The control of termites is a complex, expensive and time-consuming operation, and cannot be dealt with in detail here. Detection of the presence of termites can be achieved by identification of the species concerned, but will probably be apparent from the damage caused to property. In principle, whatever type of termite is responsible, the colony must be

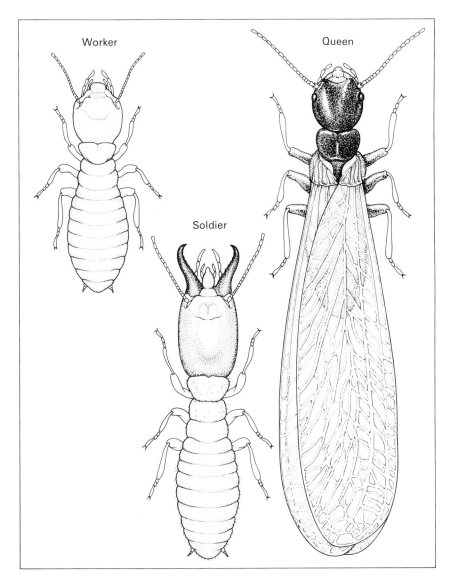

Fig. 15.6 Termite, in the Order Isoptera.

destroyed, all infested and damaged wood removed and burnt (or if damage is slight, treated with an approved insecticide to kill any termites present), and new timber protected from reinfestation. This approach, although drastic, is usually effective against damp wood and dry wood termites.

Control of subterranean termites is more difficult since the colony is much less accessible. New buildings should be protected by impregnating the foundations with an approved insecticide such as Dursban (chlorpyrifos) or permethrin. These insecticides can also be used to destroy existing colonies and live termites in lightly affected timber, either by spraying or injecting. Insecticidal gas can be used to kill live insects in more heavily infested and inaccessible timbers, although this has no residual effect. The most effective insecticides, such as chlordane and dieldrin, have a long residual life but are no longer approved for use in many countries; permethrin, while effective against termites, breaks down quickly, but if it runs into drainage systems it will be very toxic to fish. Lindane and chlorpyifos remain effective for longer.

CONE-NOSE BUGS

These are related to bedbugs in the Order Hemiptera (Fig. 15.7). They are also known as Reduviid or Triatomine bugs. Cone-nose bugs are only found in the New World from the southern States of America to Argentina. In parts of Central and South America they may transmit Chagas' disease (American trypanosomiasis) by the blood-sucking habits of both nymphs and adults, the organism being passed on in the faeces of the bug. The adult cone-nose bug is 10–25 mm in length and brownish in colour, often with red and yellow markings. The head is cone-shaped, with a long piercing proboscis hinged under the head and thorax when not in use. Two pairs of wings are folded scissor-like over the abdomen. This is large and flat when unfed, but will swell considerably after a bloodmeal. Metamorphosis is incomplete, passing through five nymphal stages lasting several months, to the adult which may live for two to three years. Nymphs and adults feed exclusively on blood and will infest domestic situations, feeding at night on sleeping hosts.

Cone-nose bugs are particularly common in sub-standard housing where they shelter during the day in cracks and crevices in wooden walls and thatched roofs. They can be controlled by improving the standards of housing, removing harbourages by plastering walls and replacing thatch with a solid roof. Walls and other surfaces should be sprayed with a residual insecticide; fogging may also be effective in driving the bug from its harbourage.

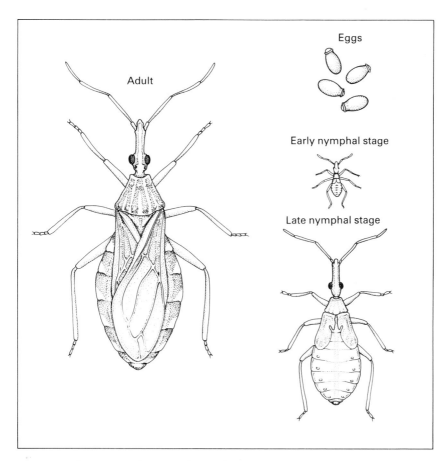

Fig. 15.7 Cone-nose bug, in the Order Hemiptera.

HARD TICKS

Ticks and mites belong to the Class Arachnida rather than the Insecta, having eight legs in the adult stage, no antennae or wings and a sac-like body. Hard or ixodid ticks belong to the family Ixodidae (Fig. 15.8). They are bloodsucking parasites of a variety of warm-blooded animals, especially cattle, sheep, deer and dogs (and even a few reptiles). Occasionally they may be picked up by humans after walking through an infested area. After hatching from the egg, the hard tick progresses from a six-legged larva, to an eight-legged nymph, and finally to the adult form (Fig. 15.9). While

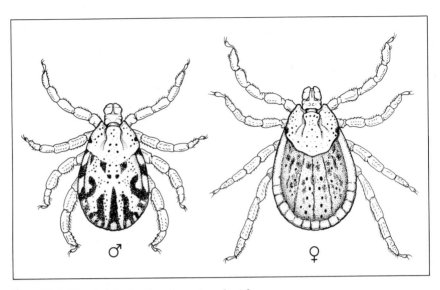

Fig. 15.8 Hard tick, in the class Arachnida.

it spends most of its life on its host, it usually drops off the animal in order to moult (Plate 36). Humans may become infested as hard ticks search for another host.

The feeding tick can be removed by cutting off its air supply by covering it with liquid paraffin, ether or chloroform. It may also be forced to release its mouthparts from the flesh by touching it with a lighted cigarette or an irritant such as insect repellent. If pulled off abruptly, the mouth-parts will break away and remain in the flesh, causing irritation (Plate 37). Ground infested with hard ticks, particularly pasture or rough ground used by cattle or deer, can be sprayed with an approved insecticide. However, this is usually not practical except over small areas, for example, for camping. Hard ticks may transmit a number of diseases such as Lyme disease, if left *in situ* for more than 24–48 hours.

FORAGE MITES

Several species of mites belonging to the family Tyroglyphidae are pests of stored products, occurring in processing plants, mills, stores and larders. These mites include *Acarus siro* (*Tyroglyphus farinae*) (Fig. 15.10), the flour mite, *Tyrophagus casei*, the cheese mite

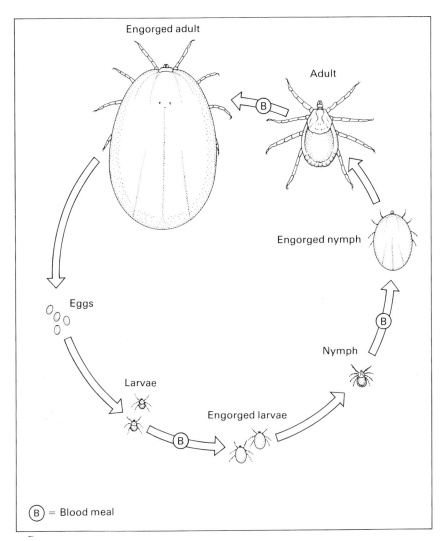

Fig. 15.9 Life cycle of the hard tick.

and *Glycyphagus domesticus*, the furniture mite. These creatures are creamy to dark brown in colour, eight-legged in the nymphal and adult stages (six-legged as larvae), but are so small that they are very difficult to see with the naked eye. They may damage cereals and cereal products, biscuits, cheese, fruit and plant bulbs on which they feed. They may be controlled by keeping the

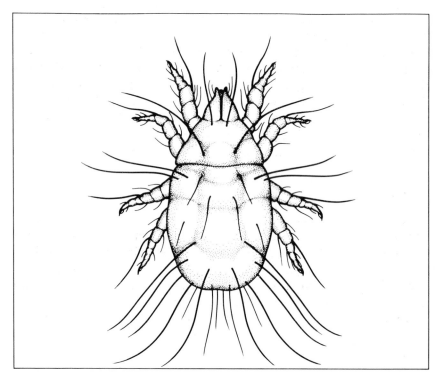

Fig. 15.10 *Tyroglyphus farinae*, one of the forage mites.

commodities dry and well ventilated (i.e. preventing the formation of moulds on which the mites feed). Heavily infested goods should be destroyed and the premises treated with an approved insecticide (see control of beetle pests of stored products).

Mites may also cause an allergic response in humans. This may take the form of a dermatitis when mite faeces, cast skins and dead bodies come in contact with the skin, and may occur in storemen, grocers, bakers and those who handle infested commodities, and even office workers handling infested paper. A particular form of asthmatic allergy will occur in sensitized people when mite debris, especially of the house dust mite *Dermatophagoides pteronyssinus* is inhaled. This mite is commonly found in bedding, carpets etc., feeding on flakes of human skin on which moulds have formed. The situation can be alleviated by thorough vacuuming and reducing the humidity of the environment.

Occasionally, mites (*Cheyletiella* species) infesting domestic pets may cause an allergic response in humans, by their bloodsucking habits (Plate 38). The cause of this can be confirmed by brushing the animal over a piece of paper (not plastic) and examining the brushings under a microscope. More commonly, this will reveal the dried coils and particles of blood defaecated by fleas (to feed their larvae) which will be the cause of the problem. The hair follicle mite *Demodex folliculorum* lives in human hair follicles, causing no problems to its host (Plate 39), whereas the scabies mite *Sarcoptes scabiei* (Plate 40) may cause a severe allergic response.

WOOD LICE

These creatures may occasionally create a nuisance by invading houses, usually after large numbers occur in the adjacent area outside. They are, in fact, Crustacea and require moist conditions in which to survive, respiring through gills on the underside of the body. They are oval and domed in appearance, usually of a slaty grey colour, clearly segmented and with seven pairs of legs when adult. Some species are able to roll into a ball when disturbed, but they will normally shelter in moist surroundings under wood and vegetation.

Invasion of domestic premises can be controlled by removing likely shelter from the building, preventing damp conditions and using an insecticide aerosol to kill live specimens (although these can easily be brushed or picked up and returned to their natural environment).

CABLE BUG

Occasionally, a situation is encountered where people are apparently being bitten and will show ample evidence of this, often scratching the 'bites' until they become secondarily infected.

Initially, the bloodsucking habits of fleas, bedbugs or mosquitoes may be suspected as the cause, or even an allergic response to a mite infestation. Yet an exhaustive search of the premises and surrounding areas, and microscopic examination of dust from vacuum cleaners and ventilation filters may reveal no evidence of arthropod involvement. The debris should be examined for spicules of fibreglass and synthetic fibres. This situation usually occurs in premises where a high level of static electricity is present (computer rooms, telephone exchanges) with nylon carpets or fibreglass insulation of some sort. The human body becomes charged with static electricity (a small shock will be felt when a metal cabinet is touched, for example). This charge attracts uncharged particles in the environment, usually on exposed skin, where they set up an allergic reaction, particularly if the sharp fibres are scratched into the skin. A simple remedy is to reduce the static electricity by increasing the humidity or treating the floor surface with an antistatic compound.

16

Vertebrate pests

CONTROL OF VERTEBRATE PESTS

A number of vertebrate animals will invade domestic and commercial premises in search of food and shelter. In doing so, they may be involved in the transmission of disease, soiling and destroying commodities and packing, damaging equipment, buildings and installations, and causing a nuisance. The most important of these pests are undoubtedly the rats and mice, but other invaders include feral birds (particularly pigeons and sparrows), feral cats, and occasionally animals such as foxes, rabbits, squirrels and moles.

The general principles of controlling these pests are similar. The infestation should be controlled by removing or killing the pest. Then, whatever is attracting the pest should be removed, since in their own environment, where they do not interfere with humans, they cannot be regarded as pests. If the attraction cannot be removed, the pest must be denied access to it. However this is achieved, considerations of humaneness and safety to the environment must always be taken into account. In the following sections rodents, birds, cats and miscellaneous vertebrates will be discussed separately, detailing methods of prevention and control.

RODENTS

Rodents belong to the Class Rodentia (Latin: *rodere* = to graw). The front incisor teeth are deeply embedded in the jaws and grow continuously, and must thus be kept at an effective length and sharpened by continual use. Behind the incisors, on either side, there is a gap (diastema) through which rodents can eject unwanted or unpalatable material before it is ground up by the molar teeth and swallowed.

Three species of rodent are of particular significance as domestic and commercial pests, namely: the house mouse *Mus domesticus*; the common rat, sewer rat or brown rat *Rattus norvegicus*; and the ship rat, black rat or roof rat *Rattus rattus* (Fig. 16.1). While the house mouse and common rat are found throughout Britain, the ship rat is rare. The three species will all move rapidly and are efficient climbers, particularly the ship rat. They are also active burrowers. Their senses are well developed, sight perhaps least so, although they can readily detect movement. They are mainly active at night, feeding on a wide range of commodities, particularly cereals and cereal products. They will eat about 10% of their own weight of food daily. Rats require a regular supply of water, whereas mice do not. All rodents will forage in the open, although the common rat prefers to feed in confined spaces. The house mouse tends to take small samples of food from a variety of sources, hence causing wide-ranging damage.

The common rat, and to a lesser extent the ship rat, is suspicious of any alteration to its surroundings. This 'new object shyness' means that it will take several days to get used to baits or bait boxes before it will feed from them, and will take even longer to investigate a trap. The house mouse is much more inquisitive and will readily explore a new object. However, if the first meal on poisoned bait makes the rodent feel ill, it will tend not to feed on similar bait again for perhaps several months, even if the bait is not poisoned. This situation, known as 'poison or bait shyness', is a disadvantage of some acute poisons, because unless the first dose kills the rodent it will not subsequently take enough to be lethal. Multiple dose poisons with a delayed action do not have this effect. Rats and mice will groom themselves frequently, and may thus take in rodenticidal dust which they have picked up during foraging.

The morphology of the house mouse, common rat and ship rat is compared in Table 16.1, and their appearance is shown in Fig. 16.1.

Evidence of rodent infestation

A careful inspection of the premises will give a good indication of the species of rodent involved and the extent of infestation. Surrounding buildings and open spaces, as well as sewers and drains, should also be investigated. Signs to look for are damage caused by gnawing and feeding, holes, smears and droppings. Packaging will often show tooth marks, the size of which will

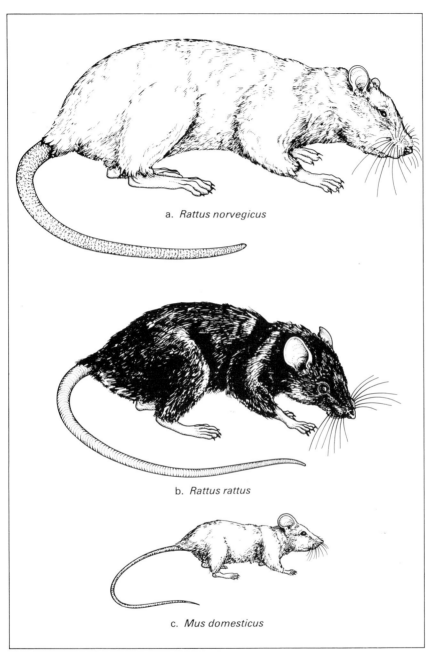

Fig. 16.1 *Rattus norvegicus*, *Rattus rattus* and *Mus domesticus*; sewer or brown rat, ship rat and house mouse respectively.

Table 16.1 Comparative table on the morphology of important rodent species

Characteristics	House mouse	Common rat	Ship rat
Scientific name	*Mus musculus**	*Rattus norvegicus*	*Rattus rattus*
Colour	Brownish grey	Brownish grey; belly fur grey	Grey black, brown or tawny; may have white belly fur
Length of head and body (mm)	80–100	200–270	145–200
Length of tail (mm)	80–100	165–205	250
Weight (g)	14–20	200–500	200–300
Build	Slender and small	Large and thickset	Slender and smaller; streamlined
Shape of nose	Pointed	Blunt	Pointed
Ears	Large, hairy	Short-thick, opaque, finely haired	Large, thin, almost hairless; translucent
Colour of feet	Pink	Grey	Pink
Shape of droppings	Small spindle shaped or irregular	Banana or sausage shaped	Ellipsoid or spindle shaped

* *Mus domesticus* (= *Mus musculus*).

indicate whether it is a rat or mouse. Mice tend to nibble the outside of grain particles, leaving the core, whereas rats (with larger mouths) will often leave half grains and smaller pieces. The house mouse usually lives and nests inside the building and will gnaw holes about 20 mm in diameter in walls, partitions and floors. Holes made by the common rat in doors and walls, and the entrances to nests, are about 80 mm in diameter, and nests may be made in wall and floor cavities. Ship rats usually nest in the roof space of the building but may gnaw through doors and loft covers.

Having established the best route from one place to another, rodents tend to use it frequently. This run becomes soiled with the grease and other dirt on the rodent's fur and will be very apparent even in moderate infestations. Runs of the common rat are easiest to see, particularly out-of-doors where the ground and vegetation is flattened, although the run itself may be well hidden. Foot prints (four toes on the front feet and five on the back) are sometimes apparent on soft or dusted surfaces, as is the mark of the tail which is usually dragged behind the animal. The faeces or droppings of rats and mice are a good indication of the cause, size and duration of the infestation. Fresh droppings are soft and have a wet, glazed appearance. After two to three days they become dry and hard, and later still the surface becomes dull. Old droppings are discoloured and often covered in dust. The size and appearance of the droppings will usually indicate the cause of the infestation.

Rodent control

As with all pest control operations, much can be achieved without the use of pesticides. Removal of food, water and harbourages will deny rodents their three main requirements for survival, thus all matters of hygiene should be attended to. Repair of damage caused by rodents may be required, and proofing of the premises from further invasion is essential. However, it is important to note that this action should be left until control of the infestation has been achieved, when holes should be blocked, particularly where pipes go through walls, air vents should be covered with metal mesh and metal plates fixed to the base of doors.

Rodenticides

The infestation should be controlled with a rodenticide, before attending to matters of good housekeeping and proofing measures.

Rodenticides act in a number of ways. The most widely used poisons for controlling rodents are anticoagulants which reduce the ability of the blood to clot or coagulate, and eventually cause the rodent to die of internal haemorrhage. These may be acute anticoagulant rodenticides which can kill the rodent with a single dose, or they may be chronic, when death only occurs after a number of feeds (multiple dose).

Some rodenticides will also be stomach poisons, for example calciferol containing vitamin D2 which causes fatal disruption of calcium metabolism of the animal. An acute poison, zinc phosphide, will give off a highly toxic gas, phosphine, when in contact with moisture. Zinc phosphide may be used to control rats and mice; norbormide is only effective against the common rat (*Rattus norvegicus*), and does not affect other animals at the recommended concentration. Alpha-chloralose is only effective against mice, ideally at below 15–16°C. Single dose anticoagulants include brodifacoum and flocoumafen.

Other acute poisons include norbormide which disrupts the blood supply to vital organs, and alpha-chloralose which causes death due to loss of body heat. Multiple dose anticoagulants include warfarin, coumatetralyl, diphacinone and difenacoum. Calciferol may be combined with warfarin or difenacoum.

Formulations

As with all pesticides, rodenticides are only effective if the pest can be made to come into contact with them in the intended way. Since rodenticides will only act if taken internally, they are often presented in the form of a bait which is attractive to the rodent. The active ingredient may be combined with cereal grain or canary seed, or mixed with processed cereal as pellets or blocks. The poison may be mixed with wax in blocks which are particularly useful in wet areas such as sewers. The active ingredient may also be available as a liquid or powder concentrate for mixing into an attractive bait material. Rodents will regularly groom themselves, thus the poison may be placed as a contact rodenticide powder in infested areas, where the animal will take it up on its fur and eat it when it preens itself. Mice will naturally explore hiding places, hence tubes with the inner surface treated with a rodenticide are effective; the mouse will crawl through the tube, take up the poison on its fur and eat it when it grooms itself. Grain or pellet preparations are available in sachets (throw packs) which remain intact until the rodents attack them. This may be a wasteful method since it encourages poor use of the rodenticide.

Baiting

To be effective, baits must be readily available and attractive to the rodent, but should not be accessible to non-target animals or humans, particularly children. New object shyness can be overcome by prebaiting with unpoisoned bait. If bait trays are to be used, empty trays should be in position one or two days before even adding unpoisoned bait. When the rodents are eating freely, the unpoisoned bait is removed and the poison added. Enough bait should be placed so that a little is left over each day; this can be adjusted after the first day or two. Untreated wax monitoring blocks will give a good indication of infestation before rodenticide blocks are added. Bait boxes should always be used if there is any danger of other animals or children having access to the bait. Bait trays prevent the bait from spreading.

The amount of bait to be used and the frequency of topping up will be recommended on the product label; these directions should always be followed. Baits which have not been touched should not be removed. It may take only three or four days to control an infestation with a multiple dose rodenticide, but it can also take three to four weeks. Poisoning with acute (non-anticoagulant) rodenticides may be effective after one to two days, but they rarely give 100% control. When no 'takes' at all are occurring, all baits should be removed.

Proofing of doors, wainscots, etc. should then be carried out. The site should be inspected after a few days to ensure that there is no further evidence of infestation; if reinfestation is likely or apparent, permanent bait stations with 1–2 kg of bait should be left in position and the site inspected every few weeks. In sites where rodents are apparently not taking solid bait, a water soluble preparation of the rodenticide should be used. When using calciferol preparations and more particularly, anticoagulants, it is important to ensure a continuous supply of bait and avoid complete 'takes' by providing a generous quantity. These should be effective after seven to ten days. The ship rat, because it is more active than other pest rodents, usually requires more bait points which should be more widely dispersed.

Reasons for control failure

Lack of success in controlling an infestation is usually a result of poor application of baits. There may be too few bait stations or they may be badly sited. The stations may not contain enough bait, resulting in too many complete 'takes', or the bait itself may not be attractive to the rodent. If failure cannot be attributed to any of these factors, resistance can be suspected. There is known resistance to a number of anticoagulants in some areas of Britain, and any such suspicion should be reported to the regional Ministry of Agriculture, Fisheries and Food (MAFF) office. Resistance to Warfarin and other 'first generation' anticoagulants in mice is so widespread in Britain that there is little point in using them.

As with all pesticides, it is absolutely imperative to read the label instructions before even opening the container. These will give a great deal of useful information, including details of the best method of application, amount to use, expected speed of success, and action to be taken in case of accidental poisoning. The requirements of the Control of Pesticides Regulations and Control of Substances Hazardous to Health Regulations, regarding sale, storage, transportation and use, apply to all approved rodenticides.

FERAL BIRDS

Under the Wildlife and Countryside Act (1981), 13 species of birds are classed as pests. Four of these are typically urban in their requirements, namely the feral pigeon, starling, house sparrow and collared dove. Under certain circumstances these will need to be controlled. The remainder are mainly agricultural pests, namely the crow, jackdaw, jay, magpie, rook, wood pigeon and three species of gull (greater and lesser black-backed, and herring gull).

Urban bird pests may need to be controlled for a variety of reasons. Their nesting material may block gutters and cause drainage problems, and their nests may harbour 'bedbugs' (probably the martin bug *Oeciacus hirudinis*) and mites which will crawl into nearby human habitation and feed on humans. Feral birds may also act as passive carriers of a wide range of stored product and public health insect pests. Bird faeces will contaminate food (causing an offence under the Food and Drugs Act, 1976) and will attract flies. The secretions from fungus growing on the droppings will erode buildings. The bird faeces will soil the buildings, necessitating expensive cleaning, and will cause a danger to the public when they create slippery and dirty surfaces. A single starling will pass 40 gm of faeces every day, and flocks of 500 000 birds are not uncommon. Feral birds may act as carriers of pathogenic organisms which will contaminate food and utensils. It is known that pigeon faeces will contain organisms such as *Salmonella typhimurium* (one-third of the pigeons in Venice have been shown to be infected): the birds themselves are often reservoirs of ornithosis.

The Wildlife and Countryside Act not only defines birds considered as pest species which 'may be taken at all times'; it also controls the ways in which these species may be taken. Poisoning of birds, for instance, is illegal, although the use of narcotics against feral pigeons and house sparrows may be undertaken under licence from MAFF.

The prevention of damage by birds can be achieved in a number of ways. Good standards of hygiene, controlled disposal, closing of rubbish skips etc. will dissuade birds from scavenging in refuse areas. Well meaning but misguided people should be discouraged from feeding birds in strategic areas. Buildings can be proofed against entry by the use of plastic strip curtains over door openings and windows and the sealing of eaves and other access points. Nests should be removed from buildings, particularly in gutters and under eaves.

Other preventive measures include the use of plastic cones and gel strips against smaller birds, as well as sprung wires to discourage nesting and perching of larger birds. Buildings, particularly courtyards, well areas, cornices and statuary, can be protected by draping with polypropylene netting made of 0.01 mm strands, which renders it almost invisible and prevents birds from settling and roosting. Coordinated use of cage traps over a large area may be effective. Trapped birds should be humanely destroyed. Mist netting, which snares flying birds in a very fine mesh net, may be used but only with a MAFF licence. The use of narcotics such as seconal and/or alphachoralose in baits under licence will cause the bird to lose body heat rapidly and become immobilized. The bird must be collected and humanely destroyed to avoid public antagonism.

Shooting the birds with a suitable air rifle may offer the most cost-effective method of preventing a particular problem, but careful safety measures must be ensured. MAFF approval is not required to shoot pest species.

It may be possible to deter the presence of starlings by broadcasting distress calls, but feral pigeons, house sparrows and collared doves do not respond. On airfields, falcons are occasionally used to capture and discourage pest species, but the answer to this particular problem may be as simple as allowing the grass beside runways to grow long so that birds cannot settle and nest.

FERAL CATS

Domestic cats are often a source of great pleasure to their owners and perform a useful psychological function, as well as contributing to the control of domestic rodent pests. These cats are often neutered, thus their reproductive capacity is limited. However, abandoned cats are very adaptable and will establish themselves in areas which provide their basic requirements of shelter, warmth and food – the latter often provided by well meaning feeders.

Colonies of feral cats may average 10–20 in number and will establish themselves in areas such as factory sites, docks, industrial estates and hospital grounds. The ratio of adults is usually one male to two or three females, and each mature female (over six months old) may produce five to ten kittens annually. Many of the kittens will die, either from feline disease or lack of food and warmth, but a significant increase in the size of the colony may occur in warmer weather.

Feral cats, having little or no contact with humans, will be shy and may become dangerously vicious. They will cause a nuisance by their calls, usually at night, when they defend their territory, or during mating, and the male cats (toms) will spray an obnoxious substance to attract females.

Appendix A: Disposal of pesticides and containers (MAFF booklet 2198)

1. Pesticides must be stored in correct containers and storage facilities.

2. Try to estimate correct amount to avoid excess residue.

3. Empty the container properly before disposing of it. Rinse thoroughly and empty residues into spray tank.

4. Dispose of surplus pesticides correctly:

    a. Return to supplier;
    b. Bury, burn or use as intended.

5. Dispose of containers correctly:

    a. Local authority;
    b. Bury 18″ deep, away from watercourses.
    c. Burn in hot fire (except those in MAFF 2198 Appendix B) away from roads, buildings etc.
    d. Aerosol cans may be put in refuse bin.

Appendix B: Storage of pesticides (HSE guidance note CS19)

Statutory Requirements:

1. HSW etc Act 1974
2. COP Regs 1986
3. Fire Precautions Act 1971

Sources of Advice:

1. Local Planning Authority
2. Local Water Authority
3. Local Fire Authority
4. Local Crime Prevention Officer
5. HSE

Relevent factors for pesticide storage:

1. Suitable site
2. Adequate storage capacity
3. Sound construction of fire resistant materials
4. Suitable entrances and exits
5. Containment of leakage and spillage
6. Dry and frost-free where necessary
7. Suitable lighting

8. Suitable ventilation

9. Properly recorded and marked

10. Secure against theft and vandalism

11. Equipped and organized to accommodate the intended contents

Appendix C

PATHOGENIC ORGANISMS FOUND NATURALLY INFECTING COCKROACHES

Organism	Disease
BACTERIA	
Pseudomonas aeruginosa	Infections of:
	Urinary tract
	Upper respiratory tract
	Wounds, burns
Staphylococcus aureus	Boils, abscesses
Streptococcus faecalis	Faecal contamination
Escherichia coli	Urogenital/intestinal infections
Salmonella spp including *S. typhi* and *S. typhimurium*	Typhoid, other enteric fevers Gastroenteritis
Shigella spp	Dysentery, diarrhoea
Mycobacterium leprae	Leprosy
Klebsiella pneumoniae	Pneumonia/URTI
Serratia marcescens	Upper respiratory tract infection
Proteus vulgaris	Gastroenteric tract infection
Yersinia pestis	Plague
FUNGI	
Aspergillus fumigatus	Aspergillosis
PROTOZOA	
Entamoeba histolytica	Dysentery

HELMINTHS (worms)

Enterobius vermicularis	Pin/thread worm
Trichuris trichiura	Whipworm
Ascaris lumbricoides	Roundworms
Ancylostoma duodenale *Necator americanus* }	Hookworms

VIRUSES

Hepatitis	'Jaundice'
Poliomyelitis.	

Further reading

Busvine, V.R. (1980) *Insects and Hygiene*, 3rd edn, Chapman and Hall, London.

Hickin, N.E. (1974) *Household Insect Pests* Associated Business Programmers, London.

Muno, V.W. (1966) *Pests of Stored Products*, Hutchinson.

Service, M.W. (1980) *A Guide to Medical Entomology*, Macmillan.

Meehan, A.P. (1984) *Rats and Mice*, Rentokil.

Hickin, N.E. (1975) *The Insect Factor in Wood Decay* 3rd edn, Associated Business Programmes, London.

Service, M.W. (1986) *Lecture Notes on Medical Entomology*, Blackwell Scientific Publications.

Index